W9-DAS-121

格列佛游记

Gulliver's Travels

Jonathan Swift

Clare West　改写

杨寿勋　　译

外语教学与研究出版社
牛津大学出版社

（京）新登字 155 号

京权图字 01－96－1581

图书在版编目(CIP)数据

格列佛游记：英汉对照/(英)斯威夫特 (Swift, J.)著;(英)维思特(West, C.)改写;杨寿勋译. －北京:外语教学与研究出版社, 1996.12
(书虫·牛津英汉对照读物)
ISBN 7－5600－1158－6

Ⅰ.格…　Ⅱ.①斯…　②维…　③杨…　Ⅲ.小说－对照读物－英、汉　Ⅳ.H319.4:Ⅰ

中国版本图书馆 CIP 数据核字(96)第 24480 号

Originally published by Oxford University Press, Great Clarendon Street, Oxford
© Oxford University Press 1993
This edition is licensed for sale in the People's Republic of China only and not for export therefrom
Oxford is a trademark of Oxford University Press
本书由外语教学与研究出版社和牛津大学出版社联合出版。

格列佛游记
著 Jonathan Swift
改写 Clare West
译 杨寿勋
＊　　＊　　＊
外语教学与研究出版社出版发行
(北京西三环北路 19 号　100089)
http://www.fltrp.com
清华大学印刷厂印刷
开本 850×1092　1/32　4.25 印张
1997 年 1 月第 1 版　2003 年 7 月第 8 次印刷
印数:261001－311000 册
＊　　＊　　＊
ISBN 7－5600－1158－6/H·638
定价:5.90 元

简　介

格列佛于 1699 年开始第一次旅行，在海上遇到风暴，到了一个叫做利力浦特的国家，那儿的人只有 15 厘米高。他后来逃走了，回到家乡。可是不久又进行下一次旅行，先是到布罗卜丁奈格，然后是勒皮他和拉格奈格，最后到了更为奇怪的慧骃国……

作为一个年轻人，格列佛为人类、为他的祖国 —— 英国而自豪。他在这些奇特的国家旅行，与巨人、魔术师和马交谈，开始时他还为他们的异常主张和奇怪看法感到好笑。但是随着时光流逝，他开始困惑，扪心自问："为什么我们人类要进行战争、撒谎、诈骗、互相残杀？难道没有更好的方式生活？"

约翰·斯威夫特 1667 年出生于爱尔兰都柏林，1745 年去世。他的许多书都对当时政治生活进行了猛烈抨击，不过他自己深受人们喜爱。他把三分之一的钱财用来帮助穷人。《格列佛游记》是他最有名的作品。

1

1
A voyage to Lilliput

I was born in Nottinghamshire and was the third of five
sons. My father was not a rich man, but he was able to
send me to Cambridge University, where I studied for three
years. When I left college, I continued my studies and became
a doctor. But I always wanted to travel, and so I made several
voyages as a ship's doctor. When I married my wife Mary,
however, I planned to stay at home for a while. But after a
few years I discovered I was not earning enough money from
my patients. I decided to go to sea again, and this time I
joined a ship sailing to the islands in the South Pacific Ocean.
We started our journey from Bristol on May 4th, 1699.

At first our voyage went well. We sailed across the
Atlantic, round the coast of Africa and into the Indian Ocean.
But before we could reach the Pacific, a violent storm hit us
and drove us to the north-west of Tasmania. The wind drove
our ship on to a rock, which broke the ship in half. Some of
the sailors and I managed to get a boat into the water, and we
rowed away to look for land. But when we were too tired to
row any more, a great wave hit our small boat, and we all fell
into the sea. I do not know what happened to my companions,
but I suppose they were all drowned.

The wind and waves pushed me along as I struggled to keep
my head above water. I became very tired and soon felt I could

1 到利力浦特

　　我出生在诺丁汉郡，在五个孩子中排行第三。父亲并不富裕，不过还是能送我上剑桥大学，那儿我学了三年。我离开大学后继续学习，当了名医生。可是我总想去旅行，就当了船医，出海旅行了好几次。我娶了妻子玛丽后，决定在家呆一些时候。没过几年，我发现从病人身上赚不了多少钱。我决定再次出海，这次登上的是开往南太平洋的轮船。我们于 1699 年 5 月 4 日从布里斯托尔启程。

　　起初航行很顺利。我们穿过大西洋，绕过非洲海岸，进入印度洋。可是到达太平洋以前，飓风击中我们，我们被刮到塔斯马尼亚的西北。飓风使我们的船撞上了礁石，把船劈为两半。我和一些水手把救生艇放下水，划开去寻找陆地。我们累得再也划不动时，一个巨浪打中了我们的小船，我们都落入海水里。我不清楚我的同伴怎么样了，不过我猜他们都淹死了。

　　我挣扎着把头露出水面，而风浪推动着我漂流。我精疲力竭，觉得再也游不动了。

voyage *n*. long journey, esp by sea or in space. 航行；（尤指）航海。**want** *v*. have a desire for sth. 想要，希望得到。**discover** *v*. find. 发现。**at first** in the beginning. 最初，开始时。**wave** *n*. ride of water, esp on the sea, between two hollows, 波浪（尤指）海浪。

not swim any more. Luckily, just then my feet touched the ground. I walked out of the sea and on to a beach, where there was no sign of any people or houses. I was so exhausted that I lay down and went to sleep.

When I woke up next morning, and tried to get up, I could not move. I was lying on my back and my whole body, my arms and legs were strongly fastened to the ground. Even my hair, which was long and thick, was tied to the ground. The sun began to grow hot, and I was very uncomfortable. Soon I felt something alive moving along my leg and up my body to my face, and when I looked down, I saw a very small human being, only fifteen centimetres tall. He had a bow and arrow in his hands, and there were forty more of these little men following him. I was so surprised that I gave a great shout. They all jumped back, very frightened, and some hurt themselves by falling off my body. Meanwhile, I was struggling to unfasten myself, but just as I managed to pull my left arm free of the ropes, I felt a hundred arrows land on my free hand, and more arrows on my face and body. This was very painful, and made me cry aloud. I lay quietly, to see what would happen next.

When they saw I was no longer struggling, they quickly built a platform next to my head, and an official climbed up there to speak to me. Although I could not understand his language, I understood that they would be friendly towards me – if I did not try to harm them. By now I was extremely

4

幸亏那时我的脚刚好踩到了陆地。我从海里走上海岸，四处绝无有人烟的迹象。我已累到极点，躺下就睡着了。

第二天我醒了想起来时，却动弹不得。我仰躺着，双手双足都牢牢地固定在地上。甚至连我的头发，已经又长又密了，也被固定到地上。太阳开始变得晒人了，我很不舒服。很快我觉察到有活物沿着腿向躯体和脸爬来，我向下看，看见了一个小人，只有 15 厘米高。他手中拿着弓箭，后面还有 40 多个这样的小人跟着。我惊讶得大叫了一声。他们都吓得往后跳，有些人从我身上跌下去还受了伤。同时，我挣扎着想解开自己，当我左胳膊挣脱了绳子的束缚时，我感到有成百只箭落在左手上，更多的落在脸上和身上。这疼得我大叫起来。我静静地躺着，看接下来会发生什么事。

他们看我不再挣扎了，就迅速在我的头旁建了一个平台，一个官员爬上那儿跟我说话。尽管我不懂他的语言，我明白他会对我友善——只要我不试图去伤害他们。那时

ground *n*. solid surface of the earth. 地面。**fasten to** firmly attach sth or two things together. 将两物牢牢联结在一起。**uncomfortable** *a*. not comfortable. 不舒服的；不舒适的。**platform** *n*. level surface raised above the surrounding ground. 讲台。

hungry, so I used sign language to beg the official for food. He seemed to understand me, because immediately ladders were put against my sides and little men climbed up with baskets of food and drink. They were surprised at how much I could eat and drink. In just one mouthful I ate three of their meat dishes and three of their loaves of bread. I drank two of their barrels of wine, and was still thirsty, because that was only half a litre. While they were bringing me food, I wondered whether to pick up a handful of the little men and throw them to their death. But I was afraid they would shoot at me again, and anyway I was grateful for their kindness in giving me food and drink, so I did not move.

After some time, another official climbed up to the platform and spoke to me. From his signs I understood that they were going to move me. The King of this country (which was called Lilliput) had ordered his people to carry me to the capital city, about a kilometre away. I made signs to ask whether I could be untied, but the official politely refused.

While I was eating, a platform had been prepared to carry me. The people of Lilliput, known as the Lilliputians, are very intelligent and clever with their hands. For me, five hundred men built a special wooden platform with twenty-two wheels. Nine hundred of the strongest men worked for about three hours to lift me on to the platform, and one thousand five hundred of the King's largest horses (each eleven and a half centimetres high) pulled me to the capital. I did not know

6

我已经饿极了,就用手势语向这个官员要食物。他似乎明白了我的意思,因为立即有梯子搭在我身侧,小人们带着食物和饮料爬上来了。他们非常惊讶我那么能吃能喝。只是一口我就吃下了他们的三个肉菜、三块面包。我喝了他们两桶酒还是很渴,因为那只有半升。他们给我拿食物来时,我在想是否要抓住几个小人把他们摔死在地上。可是我害怕他们又向我放箭,而且我无论怎么说还是感激他们好心给我送食物来,所以我就没有动。

过了一段时间,另一个官员爬上平台来对我说话。从他的手势我明白他们要把我搬走。这个国家(叫做利力浦特)的国王命令他的臣民把我搬到首都去,离这大约有一公里远。我作手势问是否可以解开我,这个官员有礼貌地拒绝了。

我吃饭时,已经准备好了一个平台来抬走我。利力浦特人很聪明,手又灵巧。为了我,500人造了一个有22个轮子的特制平台。900个最强壮的男人费了差不多3个小时把我抬上平台,1500匹国王最巨大的马(每个11.5厘米高)拉着我去首都。我自己

sign *n*. mark, symbol. 符号。**sign language** using gestures instead of words. 手势语,手语。**beg** *v*. ask for(money, food, clothes, etc)as charity. 乞求。**put** *v*. move sth. 放。**wooden** *a*. made of wood. 木制的。

about any of this, because they had put a sleeping powder in my wine, and I was in a deep sleep.

The King had decided I would stay in the largest available building, just outside the city gates. Its door was only a metre high and half a metre wide, so I could only just get inside on my hands and knees. My guards put ninety-one chains on my left leg, so that I could not escape. Then they cut the ropes that tied me and I was able to get to my feet. As I stood up, I heard cries of astonishment all around me. I felt rather miserable, but at least I could walk about now, in a two-metre circle. I was certainly an interesting sight for the Lilliputians, who had come out of the city in crowds of several thousand to see me.

Now I had a good view of the countryside. The fields looked like flowerbeds in a garden, and even the tallest trees were only two metres high.

I was soon visited by the King himself. He has a strong, handsome face, and is very popular among his people. He arrived with his Queen, his children, and his lords and ladies, all dressed in beautiful gold and silver clothes. In order to make conversation easier, I lay on my side so that my face was close to him. I spoke to him in all the languages I knew, but we still could not understand each other.

The King ordered his people to make me a bed, using six hundred Lilliputian beds. It was not very comfortable, but it was better than sleeping on the stone floor. He ordered the

并不知道这些,因为他们在我的酒中放了安眠药粉,我处于沉睡中。

国王决定让我呆在最大的建筑物里,这个建筑物就在城门外。建筑物的门只有1米高半米宽,我只有四肢并用才能进去。我的看守在我的左腿上拴了有91个环的锁链,以免我逃跑。然后他们割断捆我的绳子,我才能站起来。我站起来时听到周围一片惊叹声。我感到很糟糕,但是至少现在可以在两米之内的圈子里活动了。我肯定是利力浦特人颇感兴趣的奇观,因为有几千人成群结队出城来看我。

现在乡村尽收眼底。田野像花园中的花床,最高的树也只有两米。

不久国王亲自来看我。他脸长得坚毅、英俊,很受臣民爱戴。他是与王后、王子、公主及王公和贵妇们一起来的,他们都穿着镶金饰玉的漂亮衣服。为了会谈方便,我侧身躺下,好让脸凑近他。我尽我所知,用各种语言跟他说话,但是我们依然不能相互理解。

国王命他的臣民给我做了张床,用去了利力浦特人的600张床。这张床并不是十分舒服,但比睡在石头上要好一些。他命令

sleeping powder *n*. powder containing a drug that helps sb to sleep. 安眠药粉。 **chain** *n*. length of connected metal links or rings. 链子,链条。 **flowerbed** *n*. piece of ground in a garden or park for growing flowers. 花坛。

crowds of sightseers to go back to their homes, so that the work of the country could continue and I would not be annoyed. For a long time he discussed with his lords in private what should be done with me. I was told all this later by a good friend of mine. Clearly, such a large person could be a danger to his small people. At last it was decided that, as I had behaved so well up to now, I would be kept alive. Food and drink would be brought to me every day from all the villages, six hundred people would be my servants, three hundred men would make me a new suit, and six teachers would teach me their language.

And so in about three weeks I began to speak the language of Lilliput. The King often visited me, and every time he came, I asked him to take off my chains. He explained that first I must promise not to fight against Lilliput or hurt Lilliputians, and that I must be searched for weapons. I agreed to both these things and carefully picked up two of his officers in my hands. I put them first in one pocket, then moved them to all my other pockets, except two which I kept secret. As they searched, they wrote down in a notebook details of all the things they found.

Afterwards I read some of their report:

'In the second coat pocket we found two very large pieces of wood, and inside them were great pieces of metal, very sharp. In another pocket there was a most wonderful engine, at the end of a long chain. The engine was inside a huge round con-

围观的人回到自己的家里,以便这个国家继续运转,也不致惹怒我。他同他的臣子们讨论了很长时间如何处置我。这消息是我的一个朋友后来告诉我的。显然,如此庞大的人可能对他的渺小的臣民构成危险。他们最终决定,鉴于到目前为止我表现很好,将留我个活口。每天食物和饮料将从所有的村庄给我送来,600 人作我的仆从,300 人将给我做套新衣服,6 个教师将教我他们的语言。

所以大约三周后我开始使用利力浦特人的语言。国王经常来看我,每次他来,我都请他解下我的锁链。他解释说,首先我必须许诺不跟利力浦特为敌、不伤害利力浦特人,而且要搜身,看我有没有武器。我同意了这些条件,小心地把他的两个官员拈在手中,先把他们放在一个衣袋里,然后把他们移到别的衣袋里去,只有两个我的秘密衣袋除外。他们搜查时,在笔记本上详细地记下了他们找到的所有的东西。

后来我读到他们的部分报告:

"在第二个衣袋里我们找到了两片很大的木块,两者之间是很大的金属,非常锋利。另一个衣袋里有个很奇妙的引擎,在长链末端。引擎装在一个大而圆的容器里,容器一

sightseer *n*. person who visits the sights. 观光客,游人。**go back** retwn. 回,回来。**so that** in order that. 以便,为的是。**at last** in the end. 最后,终于。**take off** *v*. remove. 除下,除掉。**pocket** *n*. small bag sewn into a garment for carring things. 口袋,衣袋。

tainer, which was made half of silver and half of another metal. This second metal was very strange as we could see through it to some mysterious writing and pictures. The engine made a continuous loud noise.'

The officers could not guess what these things were, but they were, of course, my two pocket knives and my watch. They also found my comb, a purse with several gold and silver coins, my gun and bullets.

The King wanted to know what the gun was used for.

'Bring it out,' he ordered me, 'and show me how it works.'

I took the gun out and put a bullet into it.

'Don't be afraid,' I warned the King. Then I fired the gun into the air.

It was the loudest noise the Lilliputians had ever heard. Hundreds of them thought they were dead, and fell down. The King himself was very frightened. As I gave my gun to the officials to keep, I warned them to be careful with it. They allowed me to keep all my other things, and I hoped that one day soon I would be free.

半是由银,一半是由另一种金属做的。第二种金属很特别,透过它可以看到奇特的图文。引擎产生一种持续的响声。"

官员猜不出这是些什么东西。当然,那不过是我的两把小刀和表。他们也找到了我的梳子、有几枚金币银币的钱包、我的枪和子弹。

国王想知道枪是干什么用的。

"取出来",他命令我,"展示给我看它是怎么工作的。"

我取出枪,装上一颗子弹。

"不要怕",我预先打声招呼,然后朝天鸣枪。

这是利力浦特人历来听到的最响的声音。好几百人自觉魂飞魄散,纷纷倒地,国王自己也大感恐惧。当我把枪交给官员保存时,警告他们要小心些。他们让我持有其他的所有东西,而我希望不久的一天我将获得自由。

half *n*. either of two equal parts into which a thing is divided. 半,一半。**mysterious** *a*. hard to understand or explain. 神秘的;不可思议的;难解的。**purse** *n* small bag for money. 小钱袋,钱包。

2
Life in Lilliput

I was careful to behave as well as possible, to persuade the King to give me my freedom. Lilliputians soon began to lose their fear of me. They called me the Man-Mountain. Sometimes I lay down and let them dance on my hand, and from time to time children came to play games in my hair. By now I was able to speak their language well.

One day the King invited me to watch the regular entertainments, which are greatly enjoyed by him, his family, and his lords and ladies. I was most interested in the rope-dancing. A very thin rope is fixed thirty centimetres above the ground. People who want to become the King's most important officials jump and dance on this rope, and whoever jumps highest without falling gets the best job. Sometimes the King orders his lords to dance on the rope, to show that they can still do it. This sport is, of course, rather dangerous, and there are occasional deaths as a result. It seems a strange way of choosing officials.

There was another interesting entertainment. The King holds a stick in front of him, and sometimes moves it up and down. One by one, people come up to him and jump over the stick or crawl under it. They go on jumping and crawling as the King moves the stick. The winner is the one who jumps and crawls for the longest time, and he receives a blue ribbon

2 在利力浦特的生活

为了说服国王给我自由，我特别小心，尽可能表现得好些。利力浦特人很快就消除了他们对我的畏惧心。他们称我为"人山"，有时我躺下，让他们在我手上跳舞，孩子们偶尔到我的头发里来做游戏。这时候，他们的话我已经能说得很好了。

有一天国王邀请我去看定期表演，这是他、他的家人、以及他的王公和贵妇们极为欣赏的。我对他们的绳舞特别感兴趣。一条极细的绳子固定在离地 30 厘米的位置，想成为国王的重臣的人在绳上跳来跳去、手舞足蹈，跳得最高又不摔下来的人就会获得最好的职位。有时国王也叫王公到绳子上去舞蹈，以表明他们仍然能做。这种运动当然是相当危险的，因此死亡时有发生，这似乎是一种古怪的选拔官员的法子。

还有一种有趣的娱乐节目。国王手中拿着根棍子，有时上下移动。人们一个接一个地来到他面前，或者从棍子上跳过去，或者从棍子下爬过去。爬和跳的时间最长的人是胜利者，他将得到一根蓝带子系在腰间。

be careful to cautions. 注意，小心。**invite** *v.* ask sb formally to go some where or do sth. 邀请，约请。**occasional** *a.* not regular. 偶然的，偶尔的。**entertainment** *n.* things that entertains. 文艺节目。

to wear round his waist. The second best receives a red ribbon, and the third best gets a green one. Many of the Lilliput lords wear their ribbons proudly at all times. I had certainly never seen entertainment like this in any of the countries I had visited before.

Some days later a strange black thing was seen on the beach where I had first arrived in Lilliput. When the people realized it was not alive, they decided that it must belong to the Man-Mountain, and the King ordered them to bring it to me. I thought I knew what it was. When it arrived, it was rather dirty because it had been pulled along the ground by horses. But I was delighted to see that it was in fact my hat. I had lost it in the sea when swimming away from the ship.

I begged the King so often for my freedom that at last he and his lords agreed that I need not be a prisoner any longer. However, I had to promise certain things:

- to help the Lilliputians in war and peace
- to give two hours' warning before a visit to their capital, so that people could stay indoors
- to be careful not to step on any Lilliputians or their animals
- to carry important messages for the King if necessary
- to help the King's workmen carry heavy stones
- to stay in Lilliput until the King allowed me to leave.

On his side the King promised I would receive food and drink, enough for 1,724 Lilliputians. I agreed to everything at once. My chains were broken, and I was free at last!

次好的获得一根红带子,第三名得到绿带子。利力浦特许多王公都自豪地系着他们的带子。在以前到过的任何国家我肯定是从来没有见到过这类表演。

一些日子之后,在我最初到达利力浦特的海岸上发现了一个奇怪的黑色东西。当人们发觉那不是活物,他们断定那是人山的,国王命他们给我送来。我想我知道那是什么。由于是用马匹在地面上拖着过来的,东西送到时已经相当脏了。看到那实际上是我的帽子,我很高兴。游离轮船时我把它掉在海里了。

我经常向国王恳求还我自由,最后他和他的王公们同意我不需要再作囚徒。可是我不得不承诺一些事:

·在战争与和平中帮助利力浦特人;

·参观他们的都城要提前两小时通知,以便人们能呆在室内;

·小心不要踩着利力浦特人和他们的牲畜;

·必要时为国王传递重要消息;

·帮助国王的工匠搬运重石头;

·留在利力浦特直到国王允许我离开。

在国王方面,他许诺我将得到足够 1724 个利力浦特人吃的食物和饮料。我立即同意了一切条件。我的锁链被弄断了,我终于获得了自由!

be proud about showing pride.感到自豪。**beach** *n*. shore between high and low water mark. 海滩。**delighted** *a*. rery pleased.非常高兴的。**agree to** say 'yes'.同意,充诺。**promise** *v*. assure sb that one will give or do or not do sth.答应,充诺。

The first thing I did was visit the capital city. The people were warned, so that they would not be in danger. I stepped carefully over the city wall, which was less than a metre high, and walked slowly through the two main streets. It is usually a very busy city, with shops and markets full of people, but to-day the streets were empty. There were crowds watching me from every window. In the middle of the city is the King's palace. The King had invited me to enter it, so I stepped over the surrounding wall into the palace garden. But unfortunately the palace itself has walls a metre and a half high around it. I did not want to damage these walls by trying to climb over them. So I walked carefully back out of the city and into the King's park. Here I cut down several of the largest trees with my knife, and made two wooden boxes. When I returned to the palace with my boxes, I was able to stand on one box on one side of the wall and step on to the other box on the other side. I lay down on the ground and looked through the windows, right into the King's rooms. You cannot imagine a more beautiful place to live in. The rooms and furniture are perfect in every detail. As I was looking in, I could see the Queen, surrounded by her lords and ladies. She kindly put her hand out of the window for me to kiss.

I think I should give you some general information about Lilliput. Most Lilliputians are about fifteen centimetres tall. The birds and animals are, of course, much smaller than the people, and the tallest trees are only a little taller than I am.

我做的第一件事是参观都城。人们事先接到了通知，因而他们不致有危险。我小心地跨过城墙，那不足一米高，慢慢地走过两条主要大街。这个城市通常非常繁忙，店铺市场挤满了人，不过今天街道却是空的。每个窗口都有一些人在看我。城的中央是王宫。国王曾经邀我进去，因而我跨过围墙进入了御花园。不幸的是，宫殿本身有一米半高的围墙环绕着它。我不想因我的翻墙而把围墙弄坏，所以我小心地往回走出城进入国王的花园。我在那儿用自己的刀子砍倒几棵最大的树，做成两个木盒子。我带着木盒回到王宫，我可以在墙的一边站在木盒上，然后跨到墙的另一边的木盒上。我躺在地上，从窗户望过去，正好看到国王的房间。你再也想不出比这更好的栖身之处了。房间和家具精美入微。我往里看，可以看见王后，周围她的王公和贵妇簇拥着她。她友善地把手伸出窗户让我亲吻。

　　我想我应该给你们讲一些关于利力浦特的大概情况。大多数利力浦特人大约15厘米高。鸟兽当然比人要小不少，而最高的树也只是比我高一点。

danger *n*. chance of suffering injury. 危险。**full of** crowded. 拥挤的。**empty** *n*. having nothing inside. 空的。**imagine** *v*. form a mental image of. 想像，设想。**furniture** *n*. movable articles put into a house to make it suitable for living. 家具。

19

All crimes here are punished. But if someone is accused of a crime and then it is proved that the accuser is lying, the accuser is immediately killed. Lilliputians believe that there are two sides to the law. Criminals must be punished, but people of good character must be rewarded. So if a man can prove that he has obeyed every law for six years, he receives a present of money from the King. They also believe that any man who is honest, truthful, and good can serve his King and country. It is more important to have a good character than to be clever or intelligent. However, only those who believe in God are allowed to be the King's officials.

Many of their laws and customs are very different from ours, but human nature is the same in every country. The Lilliputians, like us, have learnt bad ways — choosing officials because they are able to dance on a rope is just one example.

Now I shall return to my adventures in Lilliput. About two weeks after my first visit to the capital, I was visited by one of the King's most important officials. His name was Reldresal, and he had helped me many times since I had arrived in Lilliput.

I started the conversation. 'I'm so glad they've taken away my chains,' I told him.

'Well, my friend,' he answered, 'let me tell you something. You're only free because the King knows we're in a very dangerous situation.'

'Dangerous?' I cried. 'What do you mean?'

20

这里所有的罪行都要受到惩处。如果有人受到指控而后来证明原告在撒谎，则原告会被立即杀死。利力浦特人相信法律有两面，罪犯必须受到惩处，品行好的人必须受到奖励。因而，如果谁可以证明自己连续六年遵守各项法律，他将得到国王一笔奖励。他们也相信任何人只要诚实、可以信赖、是个好人就能够为国王和国家效力。品行端正比聪明、智慧更重要。但是，只有那些相信上帝的人才能当国王的官员。

他们的许多法律和习俗都与我们的很不一样，可是人的本性在每一个国家都是一样。跟我们一样，利力浦特人也学会了一些不好的东西，因为谁能在绳上跳舞就选为官员只是其中一例。

现在我再回来讲我在利力浦特的经历。大约在我参观都城两周后，国王的一个最重要的官员来访问我。他的名字叫瑞颧沙，自从我来到利力浦特他已经帮了我许多次忙。

我首先开口谈话。"我很高兴他们已经拿掉了我的锁链。"我对他说。

"嗯，朋友，"他回答说，"让我告诉你，你之所以获释，是因为国王知道我们正处于险境中。"

"险境？"我大声问，"这是什么意思？"

accuse *v*. say that sb has done wrong. 控诉，谴责。
accuser *n*. sb who has been said has done wrong. 被控告的人。receive *v*. get. 收到，得到。capital *n*. city that is the centre of government of a country. 首都，国都。

'Lilliput has enemies at home and abroad,' he explained. 'For six years now we've had two political groups, the High-Heels and the Low-Heels. Perhaps the High-Heels were more popular in the past, but as you can see, our present King and all his officials wear the lowest heels. The two groups hate each other, and a High-Heel will refuse to speak to a Low-Heel. That's the problem in Lilliput. Now, we're getting information that the people of Blefuscu are going to attack us. Have you heard of Blefuscu? It's an island very near us, almost as large and important as Lilliput. They've been at war with us for three years, you see.'

'But how did this war start?' I asked.

'Well, you know, of course, that most people used to break their boiled eggs at the larger end. But our King's grandfather once cut a finger while breaking his egg this way, and so *his* father the King ordered all Lilliputians, from then on, to break the *smaller* end of their eggs. People who do that are called Small Endians. But Lilliputians feel strongly about this and some Big-Endians have fought angrily against this law. As many as eleven thousand people have been killed because they refused to break their eggs at the smaller end. Some of the Big-Endians have escaped to join our enemies in Blefuscu. The King of Blefuscu has always wanted to defeat Lilliput in war, and now we hear that he's prepared a large number of ships, which will attack us very soon. So you see, my friend, how much our King needs your help, in order to defeat his

"利力浦特在国内外都有敌人，"他解释说，"我们有两个政治集团，高跟派和低跟派，已经有六年了。高跟派也许过去比较受欢迎，可是你看得出来，现在的国王和所有的官员都穿最低的跟。两个集团相互仇视，高跟派人会拒绝与低跟派人说话。那就是利力浦特的问题。现在，我们得到消息说不来夫斯古的人即将进攻我们。你听说过不来夫斯古没有？那是一个非常靠近我们的岛屿，几乎和利力浦特一样大一样重要。他们和我们已经打了三年的仗。"

　　"可是仗是怎么打起来的？"我问。

　　"哦，你当然知道，大多数人过去习惯于从煮蛋的大的一端打破。而我们国王的祖父有一次这样打蛋时弄伤了手指，所以国王的父王下令所有的利力浦特人从那以后从小的一端打破蛋。那样做的人称作小端派。可是利力浦特人强烈反对这一点，有些大端派人愤怒地反抗这项法令。多达 1.1 万人因为拒绝从小的一端打蛋而被处死。有些大端派人逃脱加入了我们在不来夫斯古的敌人一边。不来夫斯古的国王早就想在战争中打败利力浦特，而现在我们听说他已经准备了大量的战船，不久就要进攻我们。所以，你看，我的朋友，为了打败他的敌人，我

home *n*. district or country where one was born or where one has lived for a long time. 家乡，祖国。**important** *a*. of great value. 重大的，非常有价值的。**finger** *n*. any of the five parts extending from each hand. 手指。

23

enemies. '

I did not hesitate for a moment. 'Please tell the King, ' I answered warmly, 'that I am ready to give my life to save him or his country. '

们的国王多么需要你的帮助。"

我一点也没犹豫。"请转告国王,"我热情地回答,"为了救他和他的国家我宁愿牺牲生命。"

3
Lilliput at war

The island of Blefuscu is only about a kilometre to the north of Lilliput. I knew that just beyond the narrow sea separating the two countries there were at least fifty warships ready to attack us, with many other smaller ships. But I kept away from that side of the coast, so that the people of Blefuscu would not see me. I had a secret plan.

From the King's workmen I ordered fifty heavy metal hooks, each fastened to a piece of strong rope. I took off my coat and shoes, and walked into the sea with the hooks and ropes in my hands. The water was deep in the middle, so I had to swim for a few metres. But it only took me half an hour to get to Blefuscu.

When the Blefuscans saw me, they were so frightened that they jumped out of their ships and swam to the beach. I then used one hook for each ship, and tied all the ropes together at one end. While I was doing this, the enemy shot thousands of arrows at me, which caused me a lot of pain. I was afraid of getting an arrow in my eyes, but I suddenly remembered I still had an old pair of reading glasses in my pocket, so I put them on and continued my work. When I was ready, I started walking into the shallow water away from Blefuscu. As I walked through the waves, I pulled the enemy's warships behind me. When the people of Blefuscu realized that all their

26

3 利力浦特的战争

　　不来夫斯古岛离利力浦特北部只有大约1公里。我知道把两国分开的狭仄海水那边至少有50只战船准备袭击我们，此外还有许多小船。可是我不在那侧海岸出现，我有一个秘密计划。

　　我向国王的工匠定做了50个很重的金属钩，每个都固定在一条结实的绳上。我脱下外衣和鞋，手中拿着钩和绳走下海水。海峡中间水比较深，所以我不得不游了几米，不过我只用了半个小时就到了不来夫斯古。

　　当不来夫斯古人看见我，他们吓得从船上跳下去游向岸边。我每只船用一个钩子，把所有的绳在一端系在一起。当我这样干着时，敌人向我射出了好几千只箭，弄得我很痛。我怕箭射中我的眼睛，不过我猛然记起我衣袋里还有副旧的眼镜，就取出来戴上继续干。我作好后，就开始离开不来夫斯古走进浅水。我在波浪中走着，身后拖着敌人的战船。当不来夫斯古人看出来他们所有

kilometre *n*. metric unit of length. 千米。**warship** *n*. ship for use in war. 军舰。**keep away** not to go near. 使远离，不接近。**take sth off** remove an item of clothing. 脱掉，除去。**behind** *prep*. in or to a position at the back of sb/sth. 在…后面。

warships were disappearing, their cries were terrible to hear.

As I came nearer to Lilliput, I saw the King and all his lords and ladies standing on the beach. They could only see Blefuscu's warships coming closer, as I was swimming and my head was occasionally under the water. Therefore, they supposed that I had drowned, and that the Blefuscan ships were attacking. But when they saw me walking out of the sea, they welcomed me warmly with cries of astonishment and delight. The King himself came down to the water to meet me.

'Everyone in Lilliput is grateful to you!' he cried. 'For your bravery, you will be one of my lords from now on.'

'Thank you, sir,' I replied.

'And now,' he continued, 'go back and steal *all* the enemy's ships, so that we can defeat Blefuscu for ever! We'll destroy the Big-Endians, and I'll become King of the whole world!'

But I would not agree to this plan.

'Sir,' I replied, 'I will never help to take a brave nation's freedom away. Lilliput and Blefuscu should live in peace now.'

The King could not persuade me, and unfortunately he never forgot that I had refused to do what he wanted. Although I had saved his country from attack by Blefuscan warships, he preferred to remember my refusal.

From this time on, I heard from my friends that there were secret conversations in the palace between the King and some

的战船离他们而去时,他们的哭叫声听来真是可怕。

当我走近利力浦特,看见国王和他所有的王公及贵妇们站在海边。他们只是看见不来夫斯古的战船越来越近,因为我正在游泳,头不时藏在水下,所以他们以为我已经淹死了,而不来夫斯古的战船正来袭击。当他们看见我从水中走出来时,他们热情地欢迎我,充满了惊讶和喜悦。国王本人则下到水里来接我。

"每个利力浦特人都感激你!"他说,"鉴于你的英勇,从现在起你将作我的一个王公。"

"谢谢您,先生。"我回答。

"现在,"他接着说,"回去把敌人的所有战船都偷过来,以便我们能彻底打败不来夫斯古!我将消灭大端派人,我将成为整个世界之王。"

可是我不能同意他的计划。

"先生,"我回答,"我永远也不会帮助剥夺一个勇敢民族的自由。利力浦特和不来夫斯古现在应该和平相处。"

国王无法说服我,不幸的是,他从不忘记我曾经拒绝做他想做的事,尽管我使他的国家免遭不来夫斯古战船的攻击,他更愿意记住我对他的拒绝。

从这时起,我从几个朋友那儿得知国王和几个嫉妒我的王公在宫里秘密商议。这些

lord *n*. nobleman. 贵族。 **attack** *v*. make an attack on sb. 攻击,进攻。**steal** *v*. take another persons property secretly without permission. 偷,偷窃。**refuse** *v*. say or show that one is unwilling to do sth. 拒绝。 **refusal** *n*. refusing. 拒绝。

of his lords, who were jealous of me. These conversations nearly led to my death in the end.

About three weeks later, the King of Blefuscu sent his officials to ask for peace between the two countries. After the Blefuscans had arranged everything with the Lilliputian officials, they came to visit me. They had heard how I had prevented the King from destroying all their ships. After thanking me, they invited me to visit their country.

However, when I asked the King of Lilliput if I could visit Blefuscu, he agreed, but very coldly. I learnt later that he and some of his lords considered I was wrong to have a conversation with enemies of Lilliput. Now I was beginning to understand how difficult and dangerous political life can be.

A few days later I had another chance to help the King. I was woken at midnight by the cries of hundreds of Lilliputians outside my house.

'Fire! Fire!' they shouted. 'The Queen's rooms in the palace are burning! Come quickly, Man-Mountain!'

So I pulled on my clothes and hurried to the palace. A large part of the building was in flames. People were climbing ladders up the walls, and throwing water on the flames, but the fire was burning more strongly every minute. At least the Queen and her ladies had escaped, but there seemed to be no way of saving this beautiful palace. Suddenly I had an idea. The evening before, I had drunk a lot of good wine, and very luckily I had not made water since then. In three minutes I

密谈后来几乎要了我的命。

　　大约 3 周后，不来夫斯古国王派官员来求和。不来夫斯古人与利力浦特官员安排好一切事之后，他们来拜访我。他们已经听说了我如何阻止国王摧毁他们所有的船只。道谢后，他们邀请我去访问他们的国家。

　　可是，当我问利力浦特国王我是否可以拜访不来夫斯古时，他同意了，不过很冷淡。我后来得知他和几个王公认为我不该与利力浦特的敌人会谈。现在我开始明白政治生活是多么艰难而危险。

　　几天后，我又有一次机会帮助国王。半夜里我被我房子外面几百名利力浦特人的叫喊声吵醒。

　　"救火！救火！"他们大叫。"宫里王后的屋子着火啦！快来呀，人山！"

　　所以我披上衣服就赶往王宫。王宫的很大一部分腾着火焰。人们爬上竖在墙上的梯子向火焰泼水，但是火势仍然有增无减。幸好王后和她的贵妇们已经脱险了，但是似乎没有办法挽救这座美丽的宫殿。我忽然有了主意。那夜前，我喝了不少酒，而且这之后我幸好还没有撒尿。只用3分钟

conversation *n*. talk. 交谈，谈话。**destroy** *v*. wreck. 摧毁，毁坏。**midnight** *n*. 12 o'clock of night. 午夜，子夜。**burn** *v*. be on fire. 着火，烧着。**flame** *n*. hot glowing portion of burning gas that comes from something on fire. 火焰。

managed to put out the whole fire, and the lovely old building was safe.

I went home without waiting for the King's thanks, because I was not sure what he would say. Although I had certainly saved the palace, I knew it was a crime, punishable by death, to make water anywhere near the palace. I heard later that the Queen was so angry that she refused to enter any of the damaged rooms ever again, and promised to take her revenge on me.

我就把火整个儿扑灭了,美丽的古老建筑得救了。

我没有等国王致谢就回家了,因为我不敢肯定国王会怎么说。虽然我肯定是救了宫殿,我也知道在宫殿附近撒尿是犯罪,罪可处死。我后来听说王后极为生气,拒绝再进入受损的房屋一步,而且扬言要报复我。

put out cause sth to stop burning. 熄灭,扑灭。
palace *n*. official home of a sovereign. 宫殿,皇宫。

4

Gulliver escapes from Lilliput

I soon discovered that Flimnap, one of the King's highest officials, was my secret enemy. He had always disliked me, although he pretended to like me, but now he began to suspect his wife of visiting me privately, and he became jealous. Of course his wife did visit me, but always with her daughters and other ladies who came for regular afternoon visits. When visitors arrived at my house, I used to bring the coaches and horses inside, and put them carefully on my table. There was a high edge round the table, so that nobody would fall off. I sat in my chair with my face close to the table, and while I was talking to one group of visitors, the others used to drive round the table. I spent many hours like this, in very enjoyable conversation.

In the end Flimnap realized that his wife was not in love with me, and had not done anything wrong, but he was still angry with me. There were other lords who also disliked me, and together they managed to persuade the King that I was a danger to Lilliput. I knew they were discussing me in private, but I was seriously alarmed when I discovered what they had decided. Luckily, as well as Reldresal, I had another good friend among the King's officials. Late one night he visited me secretly, in order to warn me.

'You know,' he began, 'that you've had enemies here for

4 格列佛逃离利力浦特

　　不久我发现佛林奈浦，国王的一个高级官员，是我的秘密敌人。他早就不喜欢我，虽然他装出喜欢我的样子，现在他怀疑他的妻子私下里来看我而变得妒忌起来。当然他的妻子是拜访过我，可是她总是和她的女儿及其他贵妇一起下午来例访。当来访客人到了家门，我常常把车马搬进去小心地放到我的桌上。桌缘的边很高，所以不会有谁掉下去。我坐在椅子上，脸靠近桌子，在我跟一群客人谈话时，别的人常常在桌上驱马。我像这样花了很多时间，谈话也很愉快。

　　最后佛林奈浦意识到他的妻子并没有爱上我，也没有作错什么事，可是他仍然很生我的气。还有别的王公也不喜欢我，他们共同说了国王，认为我对利力浦特是一大危险。我知道他们暗地里在议论我，但是当我发现他们的决定时我感到非常惊恐。幸运的是，除了瑞颥沙，在国王的官员中我还有一个好朋友。为了提前通知我，一天深夜，他偷偷拜访我。

　　"你知道，"他开始说，"你在这儿结了仇

enemy *n*. person who wants to injure sb. 敌人，仇敌。
pretend *v*. make oneself appear to be doing sth in order to deceive others. 假装，佯作。 **enjoyable** *a*. giving joy; pleasant. 令人愉快的，有趣的。 **alarm** *v*. disturb. 使恐慌，使忧虑。

some time. Many of the lords are jealous of your great success
against Blefuscu, and Flimnap still hates you. They accuse you
of crimes against Lilliput, crimes punishable by death!'

'But ...' I cried, 'that's not right! I only want to help
Lilliput!'

'Listen,' he said. 'I must tell you what I've heard, although my life is in danger if I do. They've accused you of
making water in the King's palace, refusing to take all the enemy's ships, refusing to destroy all the Big-Endians, seeing
the enemy's officials privately, and planning to visit Blefuscu
in order to help the enemy against Lilliput.'

'This is unbelievable!' I cried.

'I must say,' continued my friend, 'that our King reminded his lords how much you had helped the country. But your
enemies wanted to destroy you, and they suggested setting fire
to your house at night. Then you would die in the fire!'

'What!' I shouted angrily.

'Be quiet, nobody must hear us. Anyway, the King decided
not to kill you, and that's when your friend Reldresal started
speaking. He agreed you'd made mistakes, but said that a
good King should always be generous, as our King is. And he
suggested that a suitable punishment would be for you to lose
your sight. You'd still be strong enough to work for us, but
you wouldn't be able to help the Big-Endians.'

I covered my eyes with my hands. I had wanted to help
these people and their King. How could they decide to punish

敌已有一些时候了。许多王公对你对不来夫斯古的成功有点嫉妒，而佛林奈浦仍然恨你。他们指控你犯了反对利力浦特的罪行，罪可处死！"

"可是……"我嚷道，"那不对！我只是想帮利力浦特。"

"听着，"他说，"我必须告诉你我所听到的，尽管这样做我是冒着生命危险的。他们指控你在王宫里撒尿，拒绝夺过敌人的所有船只，拒绝摧毁所有的大端派人，私下会见敌方官员，企图访问不来夫斯古以帮助敌人反对利力浦特。"

"这真是难以置信！"我叫道。

"我必须说，"我的朋友接着说，"我们的国王提醒他的王公你曾经帮了这个国家多大的忙。但是你的敌人想消灭，他们建议晚上给你的房子放火，然后你将在火中烧死。"

"什么！"我气愤地大叫起来。

"小声点，别让人听见。不管怎么说，国王决定不杀你，那是因为你的朋友瑞颠沙开始说话。他同意你犯了错误，但是又说好的国王，像我们的国王，应该总是大度些。他建议适合你的惩罚是让你失去视力，你将仍然强壮，足以为我们干活，但是你将不能帮助大端派人。"

我双手蒙在双眼上，我曾想帮助这些人们和他们的国王，他们怎么能决定如此残酷

be jealous of sb feeling resentment of sb's achievements. 妒忌。**success** *n*. achievement of a desired end. 成功，成就。**crime** *n*. offence for which one may be punished by law. 罪，罪行。

me as cruelly as this?

'Your enemies were most disappointed with Reldresal's plan,' my friend went on. 'They said you were a Big—Endian in your heart, and reminded the King how much you cost Lilliput in food and drink. Reldresal spoke again, to suggest saving money by giving you a little less food every day. In this way you'd become ill, and in a few months you'd die. And so they all agreed. In three days Reldresal will be sent to explain your punishment to you. He'll inform you that the King has been very kind to you, and that you're lucky to lose only your eyes. You'll be tied down, and very sharp arrows will be shot into your eyes. The King's doctors will make sure that you can no longer see.'

'This is terrible news!' I said, 'but thank you for warning me, my dear friend.'

'You alone must decide what to do,' he replied, 'and now I must leave you, so that nobody suspects me of warning you.'

When I was alone, I thought about the situation for a long time. Perhaps I was wrong, but I could not see that the King was being kind and generous in ordering such an inhuman punishment. What should I do? I could ask for a trial, but I was not confident of the judges' honesty. I could attack the capital and kill all the Lilliputians, but when I remembered the King's past kindness to me, I did not want to do that.

At last I decided to escape. And so, before Reldresal came to tell me of my punishment, I went to the north of Lilliput,

地惩罚我呢？

"你的敌人对瑞颛沙的计划很失望，"我的朋友继续说，"他们说你内心就是个大端派人，并且提醒国王你要耗费利力浦特多少吃的喝的。瑞颛沙再次发言，建议每天少给你一点食物来节约钱，这样你将病倒，几个月后你将死去。这样他们都同意了。三天内瑞颛沙将被派来通知你国王对你很仁慈，而你也很幸运只是失去视力，你将被绑住，非常锐利的箭将射进你的双眼，国王的医生将确保你再也看不见。"

"这真是可怕的消息！"我说，"非常感谢你来通知我，我的朋友。"

"你必须自己决定怎么做，"他回答说，"现在我必须离开你，以免让人怀疑我来通知了你。"

当剩下我一个人时，我考虑了很久我的处境。也许我错了，但是我看不出国王下令做如此不人道的处罚有什么仁慈和大度。我该怎么办？我可以请求审判，但是我对法官的诚实没有信心；我可以袭击都城杀死所有的利力浦特人；但是当我想起国王过去对我的仁慈我就不想这样做了。

最后我决定逃走。因此，在瑞颛沙来通知我对我的处罚之前，我到了利力浦特北

remind *v*. inform sb of a fact. 提醒某人注意某事。**remind sb of sth** cause sb to remember of sth. 提醒，使想起。**ill** *a*. sick. 有病。**alone** *a*. without any companions. 孤独的。

where our ships lay. I took my clothes off and put them into one of the largest warships. I also put a blanket into it. Then I stepped into the sea, and swam to Blefuscu. By pulling the Lilliput warship behind me, I kept my clothes and blanket dry.

When I arrived, the King of Blefuscu sent two guides to show me the way to the capital. There I met the King, the Queen and the lords and ladies in their coaches. I explained that I had come to visit Blefuscu, as I had been invited. However, I did not say anything about the punishment waiting for me in Lilliput. They welcomed me warmly. That night, as there was no building big enough for me, I slept on the ground, covered by my blanket. It was not as comfortable as my bed in Lilliput, but I did not mind.

I did not spend long in Blefuscu. Only three days after my arrival, I noticed a boat in the sea, near the beach. It was a real boat, large enough for me. Perhaps it had been driven there by a storm. I swam out to it and tied ropes to it. Then, with the help of twenty of Blefuscu's ships and three thousand sailors, I pulled it on to the beach. It was not badly damaged, and it was exciting to be able to start planning my journey back to England and my home.

During this time, the King of Lilliput had written to ask the King of Blefuscu to send me back, as a prisoner, so that I could receive my punishment. The King of Blefuscu, however, replied that I was too strong to be taken prisoner, and that I

部,那儿停着我们的船只。我脱下衣服,放在最大的一个战船中,还放了一床毯子。然后我走下海,游向不来夫斯古,身后拖着利力浦特的战船,因而我的衣服和毯子没有弄湿。

我到达时,不来夫斯古的国王派了两个向导领我去都城。我见到了国王、王后及王公和贵妇,他们坐在车里。我解释说我是应邀来访问不来夫斯古的,不过我并没有提到利力浦特等着我的处罚。他们热情地欢迎我。那天晚上,因为没有够大的建筑给我住,我只有睡在地上,盖着我的毯子。这没有我在利力浦特的床舒适,不过我不介意。

我没有在不来夫斯古呆多久。只是 3 天之后,我注意到海岸附近有一只船,那是一只真正的船,大得足够我用。也许是被风暴驱到那儿的。我游向它,并系上绳子,然后在 20 只不来夫斯古船和 3000 名水手的帮助下,我把它拖到岸边。它损坏得还不算严重,能够计划着用它返回英格兰和我自己的家真是太令人兴奋了。

这时候,利力浦特国王向不来夫斯古国王写信,请求把我作为一个因犯送还,以便我接受处罚。但是不来夫斯古国王回信说我太强壮,无法拘捕,而且我不久就要返回

blanket *n*. thick wollen covering. 毛毯。**show sb the way** tell sb how to get a place. 告诉怎样到达。**coach** *n*. large four-wheeled carriage pulled by horses and used for carrying passengers. 大型四轮载客马车。**enough** *ad*. sufficiently. 足够地,充足的。

would soon be returning to my country anyway. Secretly he invited me to stay and help him in Blefuscu, but I no longer believed in the promises of kings or their officials, so I politely refused.

I was now impatient to start my voyage home, and the King ordered his workmen to repair the boat and prepare everything I needed. I had the meat of one hundred cattle and three hundred sheep to eat on the journey, and I also had some live animals to show to my friends in England.

About one month later, I left Blefuscu, on September 24th, 1701. The King, the Queen and their lords and ladies all came down to the beach to wave goodbye.

After sailing all day, I reached a small island, where I slept that night. On the third day, September 26th, I saw a sail, and was delighted to discover that it was an English ship, on its way home to England. The captain picked me up, and I told him my story. At first he thought I was mad, but when I took the live animals out of my pocket to show him, he believed me.

We arrived home at last on April 13th, 1702, and I saw my dear wife and children again. At first I was delighted to be at home again. I earned quite a lot of money by showing my Lilliputian animals to people, and in the end I sold them for a high price. But as the days passed, I became restless, and wanted to see more of the world. And so, only two months later, I said goodbye to my family and sailed away again.

自己的国家,暗地里他请求我留下来在不来夫斯古帮他,可是我已经不再相信国王或他们的官员的许诺,所以我礼貌地拒绝了。

我现在着急启程回家,国王命令他的工匠修好我的船,准备我需要的一切。我有100只牛和300只羊的肉供我旅途中食用,还有一些活动物以展示给我在英格兰的朋友们。

大约一个月后,在1701年9月24日我离开了不来夫斯古。国王、王后及他们的王公和贵妇全都到海岸来向我挥手道别。

行驶了一整天,我到了一个小岛,在那儿过了一夜。第3天,9月26日,我看见了一个帆船,并且非常欣喜地发现那是一只英国船,正驶回英格兰。船长把我拉了上去,我给他讲了我的经历。起初他认为我疯了,但当我从衣袋里取出活的动物给他看时,他相信了我的话。

我们最后在1702年4月13日到的家,我又看见了我亲爱的妻子和儿女。刚开始我对又在家里感到欣喜,我向人们展示利力浦特的动物,赚了不少钱,后来我高价把它们卖了出去。可是随着日子一天天过去,我变得烦躁起来,想去见更大的世面。所以,只是在两个月后,我又告别了家人出海航行了。

anyway *ad* . whatever the facts may be. 不管怎样,无论如何。 **promise** *n* . declaration that one will do or not do sth. 承诺,许诺。 **queen** *n* . wife of a king. 王后。 **in the end** at last. 最后,终于。 **restless** *a* . unable to be still or quiet. 不安定的,不安静的。

5

A voyage to Brobdingnag

I left Bristol on June 20th, 1702, in a ship which was sailing to India. We had good sailing weather until we reached the Cape of Good Hope in South Africa, where we landed to get fresh water. We had to stay there for the winter, however, because the ship needed repairs and the captain was ill. In the spring we left Africa and sailed round the island of Madagascar into the Indian Ocean. But on 19th April the wind began to blow very violently from the west, and we were driven to the east of the Molucca Islands. On 2nd May the wind stopped blowing and the sea was calm. But our captain, who knew that part of the world very well, warned us that there would be a storm the next day. So we prepared the ship as well as we could, and waited.

The captain was right. On 3rd May the wind began to get stronger. It was a wild, dangerous wind, blowing from the south this time. We had to take down our sails as the storm hit our ship. Huge waves crashed down on to us, and the wind drove our helpless ship eastwards into the Pacific Ocean.

For several days we struggled with the wind and waves, but at last the storm died away and the sea was calm again. Luckily, our ship was not badly damaged, but we had been driven over two thousand kilometres to the east. None of us knew exactly where we were, so the captain decided to contin-

5 到布罗卜丁奈格

　　我于 1702 年 6 月 20 日离开布里斯托尔,搭乘一艘驶往印度的船。直到我们到达南非好望角,天气一直有利于航行。在好望角,我们登陆取了淡水,不过我们不得不留在那儿过冬,因为船需要维修,船长也生病了。春天里我们离开了非洲绕着马达加斯加岛进入印度洋。4 月 19 日起从西边来的风开始猛烈地刮起来了,我们被刮到了摩鹿加群岛以东。5 月 2 日风停了,海面又恢复了平静。可是我们的船长警告我们,第二天还会有风暴,他对这一部分世界了解得很清楚,所以我们尽可能把船检修好,准备迎战。

　　船长说对了。5 月 3 日风势渐猛,这是非常狂乱、危险的风,这次从南面刮来。风暴袭来时,我们不得不取下风帆。巨大的海浪向我们砸来,风把我们无助的船向东刮进了太平洋。

　　我们与风浪搏斗了好几天,最后风暴平息,海面再次恢复平静。幸运的是,我们的船损坏得并不严重,不过我们被风刮得向东走了 2000 多公里,谁也说不清我们的具体位置,船长决定继续向东行驶,那是我们从

cape *n*. piece of high land sticking out into the sea. 海角。**the Cape of Good Hope** 好望角。**ocean** *n*. mass of salt water that covers most of the earth. 洋,海洋。**island** *n*. piece of land surrounded by water. 岛。**strong** *a*. solid. 强壮的,茁壮的。

ue sailing eastwards, where we had never been before. We sailed on for another two weeks.

Finally, on 16th June, 1703, we saw a large island with a small piece of land joined to it. I later discovered that this country was called Brobdingnag. The captain sent some of his sailors in a boat to land there and bring back some fresh water. I went with them because I was interested in seeing a new country. We were delighted to be on land again, and while the men looked for a river or a lake, I walked for about a kilometre away from the beach.

When I returned, to my astonishment I saw that the sailors were already in the boat. They were rowing as fast as they could towards the ship! I was going to shout to tell them they had forgotten me, when suddenly I saw a huge creature walking after them into the sea. I realized he could not catch them, because they had nearly got to the ship, but I did not wait to see the end of that adventure. I ran away from him as fast as possible, and did not stop until I found myself in some fields. The grass was about seven metres high, and the corn about thirteen metres high. It took me an hour to cross just one field, which had a hedge at least forty metres high. The trees were much taller than that. Just as I was trying to find a hole in the hedge, so that I could get into the next field, I saw another giant coming towards me. He seemed as tall as a mountain, and every one of his steps measured about ten metres.

In fear and astonishment I hid in the corn, and hoped he

来没有到过的。我们向前又行驶了两周。

最后，在 1703 年 6 月 16 日我们看见了一个大岛，还有一小片陆地与它相连。我后来得知这个国度叫布罗卜丁奈格。船长派几个水手乘一只小船登陆取些淡水，我和他们一起去，因为我对看看一个新国家很有兴趣。再次登上陆地，大家都很兴奋，在他们找河流或湖泊时，我离开岸边向里走了大约 1 公里。

当我回来时，我惊讶地看见水手们已经在船上，他们正拼命地划向轮船！我正要大喊一声他们落下了我，却发现一个庞然大物朝他们追去。我看得出他已经追不上他们了，因为他们已经快到轮船，不过我并没有等着看最后的结果。我尽快地跑开他，直到进入某种田野才停下来。田里草有 7 米左右高，玉米有大约 13 米高。我费了一个小时才走过一块田地，周围的树篱有至少 40 米高，树远比这高。正当我要在树篱中找个洞，以便我能进入下一块田地时，却看见另一个巨人向我走来。他看起来像一座山那么高，每跨一步都有 10 米左右。

我又惊又怕，躲在玉米地里，希望他不会

sail *v*. travel on water in a ship. 乘船水上旅行。 **week** *n*. period of seven days. 星期，周。 **be delighted at sth** very pleased. 高兴的，快乐的。 **run away from sth** try to avoid sth because one is lacking in confidence. 躲避。

would not notice me. He shouted in a voice like thunder, and seven other giants appeared. They seemed to be his servants. When he gave the order, they began to cut the corn in the field where I was hiding. As they moved towards me, I moved away, but at last I came to a part of the field where rain had knocked down the corn. There was no longer anywhere for me to hide, and I knew I would be cut to pieces by the giants' sharp knives. I lay down and prepared to die. I could not stop myself thinking of Lilliput. There, I myself had been a giant, an important person who had become famous for helping the people of that small country. Here, it was the opposite. I was like a Lilliputian in Europe, and I began to understand how a very small creature feels.

Suddenly I noticed that one of the giants was very close to me. As his huge foot rose over my head, I screamed as loudly as I could. He looked around on the ground, and finally saw me. He stared at me for a moment, then very carefully, he picked me up with finger and thumb and looked at me. I was now twenty metres up in the air, and I desperately hoped he would not decide to throw me to the ground. I did not struggle, and spoke politely to him, although I knew he did not understand any of my languages. He took me to the farmer, who soon realized that I was not an animal, but an intelligent being. He carefully put me in his pocket and took me home to show to his wife. When she saw me, she screamed and jumped back in fear, perhaps thinking I was an insect.

注意到我。他像打雷似地喊了一声，另外7个巨人出现了，他们似乎是他的仆人。他发出命令后，他们就开始砍我躲的这块地的玉米。他们向我移近，我就移开，最后我退到了雨水把玉米弄倒了的地方，再也没处可藏，我知道我会被巨人的利刃割成碎片，我躺下等死。我不禁想起利力浦特，在那儿我自己是个巨人，举足轻重，因为帮小国家人的忙而闻名。这里正好相反，我像是利力浦特人到了欧洲，我开始理解一个小生命的感受。

突然我发现其中一个巨人离我很近。当他的大脚提到我的头上时，我竭力尖叫起来。他向地上四处看，终于看见我了。他盯了我一会儿，然后非常小心地用指头和拇指拈起我来看。我现在离地20米，我急切地希望他不会把我往地上摔。我没有挣扎，而是礼貌地对他说话，虽然我知道他不会听懂我的任何语言。他把我拿到了农场主面前，后者很快就明白了我不是动物，而是一个智慧生命。他小心地把我放在衣袋里，把我拿回家给他妻子看。她看见我时尖叫了起来，害怕得躲了回去，也许她以为我是个昆虫，不

thunder *n*. loud noise that follows a flash of lightning. 雷，雷声。**move** *v*. be in motion. 移动。**piece** *n*. any of the portion into which sth breaks. 碎片。**famous for sth.** know to very many people. 著名的，出名的。

But in a little while she became used to me, and was very kind to me.

过一会儿后她就习惯了我，并且对我很仁
慈。

6
Gulliver and his master

S oon after we arrived, the whole family sat down at the table for dinner. There was a large piece of meat on a plate about eight metres across. The farmer put me on the table, with some small pieces of bread and meat in front of me. I was very frightened of falling off the edge of the table, which was ten metres from the ground. The farmer and his family were delighted to watch me eating food with my own small knife and fork. But when I started walking across the table to the farmer, his youngest son, a boy of about ten, picked me up by the legs. He held me so high in the air that my whole body trembled. Fortunately his father took me away at once, and angrily hit the boy hard on the head. But I remembered how cruel children can be to small animals, and I did not want the boy to take his revenge on me. So I fell on my knees and asked them not to punish the child any more. They seemed to understand.

Just then I heard a noise behind me. It sounded like twelve machines running at the same time. I turned my head and saw a huge cat, three times larger than one of our cows. The farmer's wife held it in her arms, so that it could not jump at me. But in fact, because I showed no fear, there was no danger, and the cat even seemed a little afraid of me.

At the end of dinner, a servant came in with the farmer's

6 格列佛和他的主人

我们到达不久，全家人坐在桌前吃饭。一个直径大约有 8 米的盘子上放着一块巨大的肉。农场主把我放在桌上，我面前放着些小片面包和肉。我非常害怕从桌缘掉下去，这离地有 10 米高。农场主和他的家人看着我用自己的刀叉吃饭感到很有趣。我开始朝农场主走去时，他的小儿子，一个大约 10 岁的男孩，抓住我的腿提了起来。他把我举在高空中，我全身都在发抖。幸好他的父亲马上把我拿走了，并且生气地重重地打他的头。我想起小孩子们对小动物会有多么残酷，我可不想他找我报复，所以就双膝跪下，请求他们不要再惩罚这个孩子。他们似乎理解了我的意思。

正在那时，我听见背后发出一个响声，听起来就像十几台机器同时在运转。我扭过头，看见一只巨大的猫，比我们的母牛还大 3 倍。农场主的妻子把它抱在怀里，以免它向我跳来。但事实上因为我显得一点也不害怕，根本就没有危险，而这猫看起来倒有点怕我。

用餐快结束时，一个仆人抱着农场主的

family n. group consisting of parents and their children. 家，家庭。**sit down** place sb in a sitting position. 坐下。**take sb/sth away** remove sb/sth from. 拿去，拿开。**animal** n. living thing that can feel and move voluntarily. 动物。**servant** n. person who works in sb else's house hold for wages. 用人，仆人。

one-year-old son in her arms. He immediately started crying and screaming, because he wanted to play with me. His mother smiled and put me in his hand. When he picked me up and put my head in his mouth, I shouted so loudly that he dropped me. Luckily, I was not hurt, but it showed me how dangerous life was going to be in Brobdingnag.

After eating, the farmer, or my master, as I shall now call him, went back to his work in the fields. I think he told his wife to take good care of me, because she put me carefully on her bed and locked the bedroom door. I was exhausted, and slept for two hours.

When I woke up, I felt very small and lonely in such a huge room, and on such a large bed. Suddenly I saw two huge rats run towards me across the bed. One came right up to my face, so I pulled out my sword and cut open his stomach. The other ran away at once. I walked up and down on the bed, to control my trembling legs, and looked at the dead rat. It was as large as a big dog, and its tail measured two metres. When my master's wife came into the room some time later, I showed her how I had killed the rat. She was delighted that I was not hurt, and threw the dead rat out of the window.

My master had a daughter who was about nine years old. She was given the special responsibility of taking care of me, and I owe her my life. During my stay in her country we were always together, and she saved me from many dangerous situations. I called her Glumdalclitch, which means 'little nurse'.

54

一岁儿子进来。他立即又哭又叫,因为他想跟我玩。他妈妈笑了,把我放在他的手中。他抓起我,把我的头往他嘴里塞,我大声吼叫,他松了手,幸好我没有受伤,但是这表明了我在布罗卜丁奈格的生活将是多么的危险。

饭后,农场主或者说我的主人,从现在起我将这样称呼他,又回到田野里干他的活。我想他已经告诉了他的妻子好好照看我,因为她小心地把我放在她的床上,并且锁上了卧室的门。我已精疲力尽,就睡了两个小时。

当我醒来时,我感到在如此大的房间里、在如此大的床上自己非常渺小而孤独。突然我看见两只巨大的老鼠穿过床向我奔来,一只正好跑向我的脸,我拔出剑刺破了它的肚皮,另一只立即跑开了。我在床上走来走去,以控制我不住颤抖的双腿,看着这只死老鼠。这只老鼠足有一条大狗那么大,尾巴有两米长。我主人的妻子后来进了房间,我向她表演我是怎样杀死老鼠的。她对我没有受到伤害感到高兴,把死老鼠扔出了窗外。

我的主人有个女儿,大约 9 岁,让她特别负责照看我,全亏她我才能活下来。我呆在她的国家的日子里,我们总是在一起,她许多次把我救出危险。我叫她葛兰达克利赤,意思是"小保姆"。她善于针线活,用最薄

play with sb handle sb in a casual irresponsible way. 摆弄. **arm** *n*. either of the two limbs of the human body, from the shoulder to the hand. 臂. **kill** *v*. cause death. 致死,杀死.

She was good at sewing, and managed to make some clothes for me in the thinnest material available. She also made me a small bed, which was placed on a shelf too high for rats to reach. Perhaps the most useful thing she did was to teach me the language, so that in a few days I could speak it quite well.

Soon all my master's neighbours were talking about the strange little creature he had found in a field. One of them came to see me, and as I walked towards him across the table, he put on his glasses. His eyes behind the glasses looked like the full moon shining into two windows. I thought this was very funny, and laughed loudly. Unfortunately, that made him very angry. I heard him whispering to my master all evening, and I was sorry I had laughed at him.

Next day Glumdalclitch came to me in tears.

'You'll never guess what's happened!' she told me sadly. 'Our neighbour has advised Father to show you to people, for money! Father's going to take you to market tomorrow, where there'll be crowds of people ready to pay for entertainment! I'm so ashamed! And perhaps you'll get hurt! Other people won't be as careful with you as I am!'

'Don't worry, Glumdalclitch,' I replied. 'As I'm a stranger here, I don't mind being shown to people like a strange wild animal. I must do what your father wants.' I was secretly hoping I would one day find a way of escaping and returning to my own country.

So the next day my master and his daughter got on their

的布料给我做了一些衣服,还给我做了个小床,把它放在一个架子上,高得老鼠够不着。也许她做得最有用的事是教我他们的语言,所以几天后我就能说得相当不错了。

不久我主人的邻居都在谈论他在田野里发现的奇怪小生物。其中有一个来看我,我在桌子上向他走去,他戴上了眼镜,镜片后的眼睛就像满月照进两扇窗户。我觉得这很滑稽,就大声笑了。不幸的是,这令他很生气,我听见他跟我的主人一整夜都在咕咕唧唧,我对嘲笑他感到很抱歉。

第二天葛兰达克利赤满面泪痕地来到我跟前。

"你绝不会猜到发生了什么事!"她哀伤地对我说,"我们的邻居建议父亲把你拿去展出,为了钱!父亲明天将把你带到市场上,那儿有成群的人愿意掏钱取乐!这太可耻了!而且你可能会受伤!别的人可没有我对你那样小心!"

"不要担心,葛兰达克利赤,"我回答说,"由于我在这儿是个生人,我不介意像个稀奇的野生动物那样展出。我必须按你父亲所想的去做。"我暗地里希望有朝一日能找到逃跑的路回到我自己的国家。

这样第二天我的主人和他的女儿骑上

place *v*. put sth in a particular place. 把…放在,放置。 **tear** *n*. drop of salty water coming from the eye. 泪,泪水。 **market** *n*. gathering of people for buying and selling goods. 集市,市场。

huge horse. Glumdalclitch carried me inside a small box, which had air-holes so that I could breathe. When we arrived at the market town, my master hired the largest room in the public house, and placed me upon the table there. His daughter stayed close to me to make sure that nobody hurt me. I was told to speak in their language, pull out my sword, drink from a cup, and do other things to amuse the crowd. Only thirty people were allowed in to see me at one time. On that first day everybody wanted to see me, and I was shown to over three hundred and fifty people.

My master's plan was so successful that he arranged to show me again on the next market day. I did not look forward to this at all. I was so tired with the journey and the entertainment that I could only walk and speak with difficulty for the next three days. Even when we were at home, neighbours and friends from all parts of the country came to look at me, and my master made me work hard to amuse them. So I had almost no rest.

My master finally realized that he could make a fortune by showing me to people all over the country. So about two months after my arrival in Brobdingnag, we left the farm and started our journey to the capital. As before, Glumdalclitch came with us, to take care of me. On the way we stopped in many towns and villages, so that I could be shown to people. At last, after a journey of nearly five thousand kilometres, we arrived at the capital. Now I had to work even harder, as people came to look at me ten times a day.

了他们庞大的马。葛兰达克利赤用一个小盒子带着我，上面有透气孔以便我呼吸。我们到达市镇后，主人在客栈包了个最大的房间，把我放在那儿的桌子上，他的女儿站得离我很近，以保证没人伤着我。我受命用他们的语言说话，拔出我的剑，用杯子喝，以及做其他一些事来逗乐围观的人。每次只让30个人进去看我。第一天每个人都想看我，我被展给了350多人看。

我主人的计划是如此成功，他安排了在下次集日再来展出我。我一点也不盼望这样，我由于旅途和娱乐而累得随后三天说话走路都很吃力。就是我们在家里时，邻居和来自全国各地的朋友来看我，我的主人让我卖力干活以逗乐他们。所以我几乎没有休息。

我的主人终于意识到他可以把我拿到全国各地展出而大赚一笔。这样大约在我来到布罗卜丁奈格后两个月，我们离开了农场，启程去都城。和以前一样，葛兰达克利赤一起去，好照料我。路上我们在许多的城镇和村庄停留，以便我能展给人们看。最后，在旅行了几乎5000公里后我们终于到达了都城。现在我必须更卖力地干活，因为每天来看我的人是以前的10倍。

make sure that do sth to ensure that sth happens. 设法落实。**pull sth out** remove sth by pulling. 拔出，抽出。**country** *n* . nation. 国，国家。**look at sth** examine sth closely. 观察，检察。

7
At the King's palace

Although Glumdalclitch tried to make things as comfortable as possible for me, such an exhausting life was beginning to have a bad effect on my health. I was becoming thinner and thinner. When my master noticed this, he thought I would not live much longer. But it was clear that he wanted to make as much money out of me as he could. While he was thinking how to do this, he was asked to bring me to the palace. The Queen and her ladies had heard about me and wanted to see me. When we arrived in front of the Queen, I fell on my knees and begged to be allowed to kiss her foot. But she kindly held out her hand to me. I took her little finger in both my arms, and put it very politely to my lips.

She seemed very pleased with me, and finally she said, 'Would you enjoy living here in the palace, do you think?'

'Great queen,' I answered, 'I must do what my master wants, but if I were free, I would want to spend my whole life obeying your orders.'

She immediately arranged to buy me from my master. He was delighted to receive a good price for me, especially as he felt sure I would not live longer than a month. I also begged the Queen to let Glumdalclitch stay with me, because she had always taken such good care of me. The Queen agreed, and Glumdalclitch could not hide her happiness.

7　在王宫里

　　尽管葛兰达克利赤尽可能使一切对我来说舒适些,如此使人精疲力尽的生活对我的健康还是开始产生了不良影响,我越来越瘦了。当主人注意到这点,他认为我活不长了,但是他显然想从我身上捞到尽可能多的钱。他正在考虑怎么做到这一点时,他被要求带我进宫。王后和她的贵妇听说了我,想见见我。当我们到达王后的面前,我双膝跪下,请求吻她的脚,但是她仁慈地把手伸给了我。我双臂抱着她的小指,非常礼貌地放到我的双唇上。

　　她似乎对我很高兴,最后她说,"你觉得,你会喜欢住在宫里吗?"

　　"伟大的王后,"我回答说,"我必须按我主人的要求做,不过要是我是自由的话,我愿意一生都听从您的使唤。"

　　她马上安排从我的主人那儿买过我。他非常高兴我能卖到好价钱,特别是他很肯定我活不过一个月。我也请求王后让葛兰达克利赤留下来陪我,因为她照料我一直照料得很好。王后同意了,葛兰达克利赤也掩饰不住她的喜悦。

as...as... to the same extent. 同 … 一样的。 **effect** *n*. resul or outcome. 结果, 效果。**master** *n*. employer. 主人,雇主。 **pleased with** show satisfaction. 欣喜的, 满意的。 **hold sth out** offer. 给予。

When my master had left the palace alone, the Queen said to me, 'Why didn't you say goodbye to him? And why did you look at him so coldly?'

'Madam, I must tell you,' I replied, 'that since he found me, my master has used me as an easy way of making money for himself. He's made me work so hard that I feel tired and ill. He's sold me to you only because he thinks I'm going to die soon. But I feel better already, now that I belong to such a great and good queen.'

The Queen was clearly surprised to hear such intelligent words from such a small creature, and decided to show me to her husband. When the King saw me, he thought at first that I must be a mechanical toy. However, when he heard my answers to his questions, he realized I must be alive, and he could not hide his astonishment.

To discover what kind of animal I was, he sent for three of his cleverest professors. After looking at me carefully, they decided that I was a creature outside the laws of nature. I was much too small to climb their trees, or dig their fields, or kill and eat their animals. They could not understand where I had come from, or how I could possibly survive. And when I told them that in my country there were millions just like me, they did not believe me, but just smiled. However, the King was more intelligent than they were. After speaking to Glumdal-clitch and questioning me again, he realized that my story must be true.

当我的主人独自离开王宫后，王后对我说，"你为什么不对他说再见？你为什么那样冷冷地看着他？"

"夫人，我必须告诉你，"我回答说，"自从他发现了我，他就把我当作他赚钱的捷径，他让我如此努力地干活，我感到疲劳、要病倒似的。他把我卖给你只是因为他认为我不久就要死去。不过我已经感觉好多了，因为我是属于如此伟大而善良的王后。"

王后显然对于从如此小的生物之口听到如此聪明的言辞感到诧异，决定把我拿给她的丈夫看。国王看见我，他起初认为我是个机械玩具。不过，当他听见我回答他的问题时，他意识到我一定是活的，不禁掩饰不住他的惊讶。

为了弄明白我是哪种动物，他叫来了三个最聪明的教授。仔细看过我之后，他们认定我是一种不符合自然法则的生物。我太小，无法攀缘他们的树，挖他们的田地，或者杀死他们的牲畜吃。他们无法理解我是从哪儿来的，我怎么能够生存下来的。在我告诉他们我们国家有数百万像我这样的人时，他们并不相信我，只是一笑置之。但是国王比他们智力要高些，在跟葛兰达克利赤谈话并问我问题之后，他意识到我的故事一定是真的。

coldly *adv*. in an unfriendly way. 冷淡地，冷漠地。**way** *n*. method or style of doing sth. 方法，方式。**tired** *a*. feeling that one would like to rest. 疲倦的。**kind** *n*. type. 种类。**creature** *n*. living being. 生物。

They took very good care of me. The Queen's workmen made a special bedroom for me. It was a wooden box, with windows, a door, and two cupboards. The ceiling could be lifted off, so that Glumdalclitch could change my sheets and tidy my room. The workmen even made me two little chairs and a table, and a lock for the door, so that no rats could get in.

The Queen became so fond of me that she could not eat without me. My small table and chair were always placed on the dinner table near her left elbow, and Glumdalclitch stood near me, in case I needed her help. I ate off tiny silver plates, with silver knives and forks. But I never got used to seeing the Queen eat. In one mouthful she ate as much as twelve English farmers could eat in a whole meal. She drank from a cup as big as one of our barrels, and her knives were like huge swords. I was quite frightened of them.

On Wednesday, which is a day of rest in Brobdingnag, like our Sunday, the King and Queen always had dinner together, with their children, in the King's rooms. I was usually invited too. My little chair and table were at the King's left elbow. He enjoyed very much hearing me talk about England — our laws, our universities, our great buildings. He listened so politely that I perhaps talked a little too much about my dear country. In the end he looked at me kindly, but could not stop himself laughing. He turned to one of his lords.

'How amusing it is,' he said to him, 'that an insect like

他们把我照料得很好。王后的工匠为我做了个特制的卧室,那是个木盒子,有门窗和两个小厨柜,天花板可以揭开,这样葛兰达克利赤可以给我换床单,整理我的房间。工匠甚至还给我做了两个小椅子和一张桌子,一把门锁,这样老鼠就进不去了。

王后如此喜欢我,我不在她就吃不下饭。我的小桌子和椅子总是放在餐桌上靠近她的左肘的地方,葛兰达克利赤站在我附近,预备在我需要她时帮助我。我用小银盘子、银刀和银叉吃。不过我从来也没有习惯看王后吃东西。她一口就吃下了 12 个英国农场主一顿所能吃的东西。她用一个大得跟我们的桶一样的杯子喝东西,而她的餐刀就像巨大的剑。我很害怕这些餐刀。

在星期三,这是布罗卜丁奈格的休息日,正如我们的星期天,国王和王后总是和他们的孩子一起,在国王的房间用餐。我的小桌椅放在国王的左肘边。他非常喜欢听我讲英国 —— 我们的法律、我们的大学、我们的伟大建筑。他听得那样有礼貌,也许我谈论我可爱的祖国谈得太多了。最后他慈祥地望着我,控制不住地大笑起来。他扭头对着他的一个王公。

"多么有意思,"他对他说,"像这样的小

lift *v*. raise sth to a higher level. 提起。 **fond of** having a great liking for sb. 喜爱某人。 **elbow** *n*. outer part of the joint where the arm bends. 肘。 **cup** *n*. small bowl shaped container. 杯子。

this should talk of such important matters! He thinks his
country is so highly developed! But I suppose even tiny creatures like him have a hole in the ground that they call a home.
They argue, they love, they fight and they die, as we do. But
of course the poor little animals aren't on our level.'

I could not believe what I was hearing. He was laughing at
my country, a country famous for its beautiful cities and
palaces, its great kings and queens, its brave and honest
people. However, there was nothing I could do about it, and I
simply had to accept the situation.

The worst problem I had at the palace was the Queen's
dwarf. Until I arrived, he had always been the smallest person
in the country (he was about ten metres tall). As I was much
smaller than him, he was very rude to me and behaved very
badly, especially when nobody was looking. Once he took a
large bone from the table and stood it on the Queen's plate.
Then he took me in both hands and pushed my legs into the
top of the bone. I could not pull myself out, and had to stay
there, feeling—and looking—extremely stupid. When the
Queen finally saw me, she could not stop herself laughing, but
she was angry with the dwarf at the same time.

In Brobdingnag there are large numbers of flies in summer,
and these awful insects, each as big as an English bird, gave
me no peace. The dwarf used to catch some in his hands, and
then let them out suddenly under my nose. He did this both to
frighten me and amuse the Queen. I had to use my knife to cut

昆虫也能谈论如此重要的事情！他认为他的国家有如此发达！不过我想就是像他这样的小动物在地面也有个洞子他们自己称作家。他们争辩、恋爱、战争、死亡，跟我们一样。当然这种可怜的小动物跟我们不是在同一个层次。"

我不能相信我所听到的。他在嘲笑我的祖国，一个以其美丽的城市和宫殿、以其伟大的国王和王后、以其英勇而诚实的人民而闻名的国家。不过我对此毫无办法，只有简单地接受这种处境。

我在宫里最糟糕的问题是王后的侏儒。我到达前，他一直是这个国家最矮小的人（他大约 10 米高）。因为我远比他矮，他对我很粗鲁，他表现得很不好；特别是当没人在旁看着时。有一次他从桌上拿了一根大骨头立在王后的盘子上，然后抓着我的两只手把我的双腿推进骨头的顶端，我自己出不来，只有呆在那儿，感觉 —— 而且看起来也是 —— 极为愚蠢，王后最终看见了，禁不住笑起来，但同时也对侏儒非常生气。

布罗卜丁奈格夏天有大量的苍蝇，而这种可怕的昆虫每个有英格兰一只鸟那么大，扰得我毫无宁日。侏儒经常抓几个在手中，然后在我的鼻子底下突然松手，他这样做既是惊吓我也是逗王后乐。它们在我身边飞

nothing *pron*. not anything. 没有什么。 **rude** *a*. impolite. 粗鲁，无礼。 **plate** *n*. shallow dish from which food is served. 餐盘，碟子。 **stupid** *a*. not intelligent. 愚蠢，傻的。

them to pieces as they flew around me.

Another time, the dwarf picked me up and dropped me quickly into a bowl of milk on the table. Luckily, I am a good swimmer, so I managed to keep my head out of the milk. As soon as Glumdalclitch saw I was in danger, she ran from the other side of the room to rescue me. I was not hurt, but this time the dwarf was sent away from the palace as a punishment. I was very pleased.

I would now like to describe Brobdingnag. The people who draw our European maps think there is nothing but sea between Japan and America, but they are wrong. Brobdingnag is quite a large country, joined on to northwest America, but separated from the rest of America by high mountains. It is about ten thousand kilometres long and from five to eight thousand wide. The sea around it is so rough and there are so many rocks in the water that no large ships can land on any of the beaches. This means that the people of Brobdingnag do not normally have visitors from other parts of the world.

There are fifty-one cities and a large number of towns and villages. The capital stands on both sides of a river, and has more than eighty thousand houses. It covers three hundred and forty square kilometres. The King's palace covers about eleven square kilometres: the main rooms are eighty metres high. The palace kitchen is huge—if I described it, with its great pots on the fire and the mountains of food on the tables, perhaps you would not believe me. Travellers are often accused

来飞去,我只有用我的刀子把它们砍成碎片。

另有一次,侏儒抓起我然后迅速把我丢进桌上的一碗牛奶里。好在我是个游泳好手,所以我能使头露在牛奶外面。葛兰达克利赤一看见我有危险就从屋子的另一端跑过来救我。我没有受伤,不过这次侏儒被罚出了宫,我对此非常高兴。

现在我想描绘一下布罗卜丁奈格。绘制欧洲地图的人认为在日本和美洲之间除了海什么都没有,但是他们错了。布罗卜丁奈格是个相当大的国家,与北美相连,但高山把它与美洲其他部分隔开了。它大约有1万公里长,5 000至8 000公里宽。它周围海水汹涌,水中有太多的礁石,绝没有大轮船可以在岸边登陆。这意味着布罗卜丁奈格人正常情况下很少有来自世界其他地方的来客。

有51座城市,大量的市镇和村庄。都城横跨一条河,有8万座房子,面积达340多平方公里,国王的宫殿占地大约11平方公里,主要房屋有80米高。王宫的厨房很大 —— 如果我来描绘,还有火上的大锅和桌上如山的食物,也许你不会相信。旅行者常

keep *v.* continue to be in the specified condition. 保持。**send away** tell sb to go away. 撵走,赶走。**draw** *v.* make pictures with a pencil. 用铅笔画。**rock** *n.* part of the earth's crust. 岩层,岩。

of not telling the truth when they return. To avoid this happening to me, I am being careful to describe what I saw as exactly and carefully as possible.

常被指责在他们回家时不说真话。为了避免这种事发生在我身上，我一直留心尽可能准确、仔细地描绘我所看到的。

careful a. taking care. 小心, 当心。

71

8

More adventures in Brobdingnag

Because I was so small, I had several dangerous accidents during my stay at the palace. One day Glumdalclitch put me down on the grass in the palace garden, while she went for a walk with some of the Queen's ladies. A small white dog which belonged to one of the gardeners appeared, and seemed very interested in me. He took me in his mouth and carried me to his master. Luckily, he had been well trained, and did not try to bite me, so I was not hurt.

One day the Queen said to me, 'It would be good for your health to do some rowing or sailing. What do you think? Would you like me to arrange it for you?'

'Madam,' I answered, 'I'd love to row or sail a little every day. But where can we find a boat that's small enough?'

'Leave that to me,' she replied, and called for her workmen. She ordered them to make a tiny boat with sails. They also made a wooden container, about a hundred metres long, seventeen metres wide and three metres deep. This container was filled with water, and I was carefully placed in my boat on the water. Every day I used to row or sail there, while the Queen and her ladies watched. There was no wind, of course, but the ladies blew hard to move my boat along.

I nearly lost my life again, when a lady picked me up to put me in the boat. She was not careful enough, and dropped me.

72

8 在布罗卜丁奈格的其他经历

由于我太小,我在王宫逗留期间有好几次危险事故。一天,葛兰达克利赤把我放在王宫花园的草地上,自己和王后的几个贵妇去散步了。一个园丁的小白狗出现了,它似乎对我很感兴趣,它用嘴叼着我,把我叼到了它的主人那儿。幸运的是,它受到了良好的训练,没有试图咬我,所以我没有受伤。

一天王后对我说,"划船或扬帆会对你的健康有好处。你觉得怎么样?你愿意让我为你安排吗?"

"夫人,"我回答说,"我愿意每天划船或扬帆一会儿,可是哪儿找得到足够小的船呢?"

"交给我吧,"她回答说,然后叫来了她的工匠,命令他们做有帆的小船。他们还做了一个木质容器,大约 100 米长、17 米宽、3 米深。这个容器盛上了水,我被小心地放进了水面上我的船里。每天我在那儿划船或者扬帆,王后和她的贵妇在旁边看。当然没有风,不过这些贵妇用力吹,使船移动。

当一个贵妇抓起我往船里放时,我几乎再次丢了性命。她不够小心,把我弄掉了。

stay *v*. not depart. 停留;住。**belong to sb** be the property of sb. 属于,是…的财产。**gardener** *n*. person who works in a garden. 园丁,花匠。**train** *v*. bring a person or an animal to a desired standard of behaviour by instruction. 训练。

With horror, I felt myself falling through the air. But instead of crashing to the ground, I was caught, by my trousers, on a pin in her clothes. I had to stay there without moving a finger, until Glumdalclitch came running to rescue me.

But the greatest danger to me in Brobdingnag came from a monkey. One day Glumdalclitch left me alone in her bedroom while she visited some of the ladies. It was a warm day, and her window was open. I was in the box which I used as my bedroom, with the door open. Suddenly I heard the noise of an animal jumping through the window, and immediately I hid at the back of my box. The monkey, which appeared huge to me, very soon discovered my hiding-place. He picked me up, and held me close to him like a baby. When he heard someone opening the bedroom door, he jumped out of the window and ran on to the roof.

I thought I had never been in such great danger. He was running on three legs and holding me in the fourth. At any moment he could let me fall, and we were at least three hundred metres above the ground. I could hear a lot of shouting in the palace. The servants had realized what was happening, and brought ladders to climb up on to the roof. Glumdalclitch was crying, and hundreds of people were watching from the garden. Meanwhile, the monkey was sitting calmly on top of the roof. He was taking food from his mouth and trying to push it into *my* mouth. He still seemed to think I was his baby. I suppose it was an amusing sight for the crowd below,

我惊恐万状，感觉自己在空中往下落。不过没有摔到地上，我的裤子刮住了她衣服上的一个别针。我不得不呆在那儿，连一个指头都不敢动，直到葛兰达克利赤跑过来救我。

但是在布罗卜丁奈格的最大危险来自一只猴子。一天葛兰达克利赤让我独自留在她的房间里，她去拜访一些贵妇。天比较热，窗子是开着的。我正呆在我用做卧室的盒子里，卧室的门是敞开的。突然我听见动物跳过窗子的声音，我立即躲到我的盒子后面去。猴子在我看起来很大，它很快就发现了我的藏身之处。它抓起我，把我紧紧地抱着，像是抱着婴儿。当它听见有人打开卧室门的声音，就立即从窗子跳出去跑上屋顶。

我想我从来没有处于如此大的危险之中。它用三只腿跑一只腿抱着我，随时都可能让我掉下去，而我们至少离地有 300 米高。我可以听见宫里一片叫嚷声，仆从已经明白发生了什么事，拿来梯子往屋顶上爬。葛兰达克利赤在哭，数百人在花园里看。此时，猴子正平静地坐在屋顶，它正从它的嘴里取出食物往我的嘴里塞。它仍然以为我是它的婴儿。我猜这对于下面围观的人来

immediately *ad* . at once. 立刻；马上。**hiding-place** *n* . where sb is hidden. 隐藏处。**watch** *v* . look at sth. 看，观察。**below** *prep* . at or to a lower position. 在…之下，低下。

but I was in terrible fear of falling.

Finally, several servants climbed on the roof, and as they came nearer, the monkey put me down and ran away. I was rescued and brought down to the ground. I had to stay in bed for two weeks after this, before I felt well enough to meet people again. The monkey was caught and killed.

When I next saw the King, he asked me about this experience. 'How did you feel,' he said, 'when the monkey was holding you up on the roof?'

'Sir,' I replied bravely, 'I was afraid, that's true. But next time an animal like that attacks me, I shall not hesitate. I'll pull out my sword like this'—and I showed him what I would do—'and give the creature such a wound that it will never come near me again!'

But while I waved my tiny sword in the air, the King and his lords laughed loudly. I had wanted to prove my bravery, but I failed, because to them I was only an unimportant little creature. I realized later that this often happens in England, when *we* laugh at someone of no family, fortune, or intelligence, who pretends to be as important as our great leaders.

In the next few weeks, I began to have some very interesting conversations with the King. He was an intelligent, understanding person.

'Tell me more about your country,' he said to me one day. 'I would like to hear about your laws, your political life, and your customs. Tell me everything. There may be something

说是有趣的景观,可是我极为害怕掉下去。

最后几个仆人爬上了屋顶,当他们走近时,猴子放下我跑开了。我得救了,被送到了地面。此后我不得不在床上躺了两周,直到我感觉好些,才再见人。猴子被抓住杀死了。

当我再次见到国王时,他问我这次的经历。"你的感受是什么,"他问,"当猴子抱着你上屋顶时?"

"先生,"我勇敢地回答说,"我很害怕,那是真的,不过下次像这样的动物来袭击我时,我决不会犹豫。我会像这样拔出我的宝剑"——我向他表演我将做什么——"将这动物伤得再也不敢靠近我!"

可是我在空中挥舞我的小剑时,国王和他的王公大声笑了起来,我想证明我的勇敢,可是我失败了,因为对他们来说我是个无足轻重的小动物。我后来想起这在英国也经常发生,当一个没有家庭背景、没有财富或没有智力的人装模作样跟我们伟大的领袖一样重要时我们也会如此嘲笑。

随后几周,我开始跟国王有几次非常有趣的谈话。他是一个聪明、理解力强的人。

"再告诉我一些关于你们国家的事,"一天他对我说,"我想听听你们的法律、你们的政治生活以及你们的风俗习惯。告诉我这些方面的全部情况,也许有些东西我们可以

climb v. to move esp from a lower to a higher position by using the hands and feet. 爬,攀登. **roof** n. structure covering or forming the top of a building. 屋顶,顶部. **wound** n. injury caused deliberately to part of the body by cutting. 伤,创伤.

that we can usefully copy here in Brobdingnag. '

'I shall be delighted, sir, ' I answered proudly. 'Our king controls our three great countries, Scotland, Ireland and England. We grow much of our own food, and our weather is neither too hot nor too cold. There are two groups of men who make our laws. One is called the House of Lords—they are men from the oldest and greatest families in the country. The other is called the House of Commons—these are the most honest, intelligent, and sensible men in the country, and are freely chosen by the people. We have judges to decide punishments for criminals, and we have a large army, which cannot be defeated by any other in the world. '

While I was talking, the King was making notes. For several days I continued my explanation, and I also described British history over the last hundred years. Then the King asked me a large number of questions. These were some of them.

'How do you teach and train young people of good family? If the last son of an old family dies, how do you make new lords for the House of Lords? Are these lords really the most suitable people to make the country's laws? And in the House of Commons, are these men really so honest and intelligent? Do rich men never buy their way into this House? You say the lawmakers receive no pay, but are you sure that they never accept bribes?'

Then he asked questions about our lawcourts. 'Why are

搬到布罗卜丁奈格来用。"

"我很高兴,先生,"我骄傲地回答,"我们的国王控制着三个伟大的国家:苏格兰、爱尔兰和英格兰。我们的食物大部分自己出产,天气既不太冷也不太热。有两组人制定我们的法律,其一叫做上议院,他们来自这个国家最古老最伟大的家族,其二叫做下议院,他们是这个国家最诚实、聪明而通情达理的人,是由人民自由选出来的。我们有法官决定对犯罪分子的惩罚,我们有庞大的军队,无敌于全世界。"

在我讲的时候,国王作着笔记。我连续几天进行解释,我也描述了过去百来年不列颠的历史。然后国王问了我一大堆问题。这是其中几个。

"你们怎么教育、训练好家族的年青人?如果一个古老家族的最后一个儿子去世了,你们怎么给上议院选定新的议员?这些议员真是最适合给这个国家制定法律的人吗?在下议院中,这些人是真的诚实而聪明吗?富人从来不用钱买路进入议院吗?你说法律制定者不收报酬,但是你敢肯定他们从来不收受贿赂吗?"

然后他问了一些关于我们的法庭的问题。"你们的审判为什么那么耗时而费钱?

weather *n*. condition of the atmosphere at a certain place and time. 天气,气象。**group** *n*. a number of people. 群,组。**family** *n*. any group of people related by blood or marriage. 家庭。

your trials so long and so expensive? How much do your lawyers and judges really know about the laws? How carefully do they decide between right and wrong?'

'And why,' he went on, 'are you so often at war? Either you enjoy fighting, or you have very difficult neighbours! Why do you need an army at all? You would not be afraid of any other country, if you were peaceful people. And in the last hundred years you've done nothing but rob, fight, and murder! Your recent history shows the very worst effects of cruelty, jealousy, dishonesty, and madness!'

I tried to answer the King as well as I could, but he did not think our system was a good one.

'No, my little friend,' he said kindly but seriously, 'I'm sorry for you. You've proved to me that your country has nothing valuable to offer us. Perhaps once, in the past, your political life was adequately organized, but now it is clear that there is laziness and selfishness in every part of the system. Your politicians can be bribed, your soldiers aren't really brave, your judges and lawyers are neither reasonable nor honest, and your lawmakers themselves know little and do less. I sincerely hope that you, who have spent most of your life travelling, have a better character than most Englishmen. But from what you've told me, I'm afraid that your countrymen are the worst little nation of insects that has ever crawled upon the ground.'

I am very sorry to have to report these words of the King's,

你们的律师和法官究竟知道多少你们的法律？他们判定正误有多仔细?"

"为什么,"他接着说,"你们经常打仗?或者是你们喜欢战争,或者是你们的邻居很难处! 究竟为什么你们需要军队? 如果你们是热爱和平的人民,你们不应该害怕别的国家。而在过去的百年里,你们除了掠夺、打仗和谋杀没有干别的! 你们最近的历史显示了残酷、嫉妒、欺诈和疯狂的最糟糕的结果!"

我力图尽可能满意地回答国王,可是他并不认为我们的制度好。

"不,我的小朋友,"他和善而认真地说,"我为你感到遗憾。你向我证明了你们没有什么有价值的东西提供给我们。也许在过去,你们的政治生活曾经组织得恰当,可是现在很明显,这个制度的每一部分都充满了惰性和自私。你们的政客可以受贿赂,你们的战士并不真的勇敢,你们的法官和律师既不通情理也不诚实,而你们的法律制定者自己知道得很少,做得更少。你一生的大多数时光都用于旅行了,我真诚地希望你比大多数英国人品行要好,不过据你所告诉我的,我担心你的国人是地上曾经爬行过的昆虫中最糟糕的小国民。"

我非常遗憾不得不转述国王的这些话,

expensive *a*. cosing a lot of money. 昂贵的。**lawyer** *n*. person who is trained and qualified in legal matters.律师。**either or** *conj*. used to show a choice of two alternatives. 不是…便是。**afraid** *a*. full of fear. 害怕,畏惧。

and I only do so because of my love of the truth. I must tell you exactly what happened, even if I do not agree with it. I had to listen patiently, while he was giving his extraordinary opinions of my dear country. We must remember, however, that this King lives in a country almost completely separate from the rest of the world. Because he does not know other countries' systems or customs, he has a certain narrowness of thinking, which we Europeans do not have, of course.

You will find it difficult to believe what happened next.

'Sir,' I said, 'I'd like to give you something to thank you for your kindness to me since I arrived at the palace. Three or four hundred years ago, we Europeans discovered how to make a special powder. When you set fire to it, it burns and explodes immediately, with a noise louder than thunder. You can use it to shoot heavy balls of metal from large guns. It can destroy the largest ships, it can kill a whole army, it can cut men's bodies in half, it can destroy the strongest walls. It's called gunpowder, and it's easy and cheap to make. To show you how grateful I am to you, I'm offering to explain how to make it—then you will be able to destroy all your enemies!'

I was very surprised by the King's reply.

'No!' he cried in horror. 'Don't tell me! I don't want to know how to murder people like that. I would rather give half my country away than know the secret of this powder. How can a tiny creature like you have such inhuman, cruel ideas? Never speak to me of this again!'

我这样做只是因为我对真相的热爱。我必须原原本本地告诉你们发生的事,即使我并不赞同。在他发表关于我亲爱的祖国的不同寻常的看法时,我不得不耐心地听着。不过我们必须记住,这个国王生活在几乎完全与世隔绝的国度里,因为他不知道别的国家的制度或习俗,他的想法中有一定的狭隘性,这当然是我们欧洲人所没有的。

你将觉得接下来发生的事很难置信。

"先生,"我说,"我想送给你一样东西以表示感谢自我从来到宫里后你对我的厚爱。三四百年前,我们欧洲人发明了怎样制造一种特别的粉末。当你点燃它时,它立即燃烧爆炸,声音比打雷还响,你可以用它来把很沉的金属弹丸从很大的枪中射出,它可以摧毁最大的轮船,消灭整个军队,把人的身躯切成两半,摧毁最坚固的墙壁。它叫火药,制作起来简单廉价。为了表达我是多么的感激你,我自愿给你解释怎么制造它——然后你就有能力消灭你的所有敌人!"

我对国王的回答感到非常吃惊。

"不!"他惊恐地叫道,"不要告诉我!我不想知道怎样去谋杀人。我宁愿割出一半国土也不想知道这种粉末的秘密。你们这样渺小的生物怎么可以有如此不人道、残酷的想法?决不要再跟我提这事!"

because *conj.* for the reason that. 因为。**separate from** *v.* to move apart. 分,分开。**arrive** *v.* reach a place. 到达,抵达。**set fire to sth** light sth. 点燃,点火。**gunpowder** *n.* explosive powder used in guns.火药。**like** *prep.* similar to sth.象,类似,和…一样。

How strange that such an excellent king should not take the chance I was offering him! No European king would hesitate for a moment. But he had other strange ideas. He believed, very simply, that every problem can be solved by honest, sensible people, and that the political life of a country must have no secrets and must be open for all to see and understand. Of course, we know that this is impossible, so perhaps his opinion of us is not worth considering.

多么奇怪！如此优秀的国王，竟然不抓住我提供给他的机会！任何一个欧洲国王绝不会有一丝犹豫。可是他还有其他怪念头。他相信，每个问题都可以被诚实、通情理的人解决，一个国家的政治生活必须没有秘密，必须公开给世人看和理解。当然，我们知道这是不可能的，所以他的看法也许对我们来说不值得考虑。

---

idea *n*. thought. 思想；主意。**solve** *v*. find an answer. 解决，解答。

85

9

Gulliver escapes from Brobdingnag

I was still hoping to return to England one day. But the ship in which I had arrived in Brobdingnag was the first that had ever come near the coast. So I could not see how I could get away. I began to think more and more about my family and my home.

By now I had been in Brobdingnag for about two years. When the King and Queen travelled to the south coast, Glumdalclitch and I went with them. I really wanted to be close to the sea again, which I had not seen or even smelt for so long. As Glumdalclitch was ill, I asked a young servant to take me down to the beach for some fresh air. The boy carried me in my travelling box, and put me down on the beach, while he looked for birds' eggs among the rocks. I looked sadly at the sea, but stayed in my box, and after a while I fell asleep.

I was woken suddenly when my box was lifted high in the air. I can only suppose that a large bird took hold of the ring on top of the box with his talons, and flew away with it. Through the windows I could see the sky and clouds passing by, and I could hear the noise of the bird's wings. Then I was falling, so fast that I felt quite breathless. There was a loud crash, as the box fell into the sea. Perhaps the bird had been attacked by others, and so had to drop what he was carrying.

Luckily, the box had been well made, and not much sea

86

9　格列佛逃离布罗卜丁奈格

　　我仍然希望有朝一日回到英国。可是我到达布罗卜丁奈格时乘坐的轮船是第一只曾经靠近此处海岸的。所以我不知道怎样才能逃离。我开始越来越想念我的家人和自己的家了。

　　这时我到布罗卜丁奈格已经有大约两年了。国王和王后到南部海岸去旅行时，葛兰达克利赤和我也一同前往。我真是想再度靠近大海，这么长时间我既没有看见也没有闻见它。由于葛兰达克利赤生病了，我叫一个年轻仆人把我带到海滩上呼吸新鲜空气。这个男孩用我的旅行盒提着我，在海滩上把我放下来，他自己去石头中找鸟蛋去了。我忧伤地看着大海，不过还是呆在我的盒子里，过了一会儿我就睡着了。

　　我的盒子被提到高空中，把我突然惊醒了。我只能猜测一只大鸟的爪子抓住了我盒子顶部的环，带着它飞走了。透过窗户我可以看见天空和云彩飞逝，我还可以听见鸟翅膀的声音。然后我往下跌，快得我觉得几乎透不过气。盒子掉进海水里，溅起很响的水声。也许这鸟儿受到什么袭击，所以不得不丢下它抓的东西。

　　幸亏盒子做得很好，没有多少海水流进

one day at a particular time in the future. 总有一天。
coast *n*. land bordering the sea. 海岸。**see** *v*. form a picture in the mind of. 想像出，想像。**get away** escape. 逃脱，脱身。**smell** *v*. notice sth by using the nose. 闻出，嗅出。**drop** *v*. fall. 落下。

water came in. But I do not think any traveller has ever been in a worse situation than I was then. I wondered how long I would survive, with no food or drink in the middle of the ocean. I felt sure I would never see poor Glumdalclitch again, and I knew how sad she would be to lose me.

Several hours passed, and then I suddenly heard a strange noise above my head. People were fastening a rope to the ring. Then my box was pulled through the water. Was it a ship that was pulling me along?

'Help! Help!' I shouted as loudly as I could.

I was delighted to hear English voices reply.

'Who's there?' they cried.

'I'm English!' I shouted back desperately. 'Please help me to get out of here! Just put your finger into the ring on top of the box and lift it out of the water! Quickly!'

There were great shouts of laughter.

'He's mad!' I heard one man say.

'*Ten men* couldn't lift that huge box!' said another. There was more laughter.

Indeed, because I had been with giants for so long, I had forgotten that my countrymen were as small as me. The only thing the sailors could do was to cut a hole in the top of my box, and help me to climb out. I was exhausted and unable to walk far.

They took me to their captain.

'Welcome to my ship,' he said kindly. 'You're lucky we

来,不过我想没有多少旅行者比我此时的处境更糟糕。我思忖着,在大洋之中,没有食物,没有饮水,我能生存多久。我确切地感到再也见不着可怜的葛兰达克利赤了,我知道失去我她将多么悲伤。

几个小时之后,我忽然听见头上有个奇怪的声音,有人正在环上系绳子,然后我的盒子在水中被拖动。是一个轮船在拖着我走吗?

"救命! 救命!"我竭力大声喊叫。

我很高兴地听到说英语的声音在回答。

"谁在那儿?"他们喊道。

"我是英国人!"我拼命地嚷,"请帮我从这儿出去! 把你的手指放到盒子顶上的环上把它从水里提出来! 快一点!"

一片轰然大笑。

"他疯啦!"我听见一个人说。

"10 个人也提不起那个大盒子!"另一个说。笑声更响了。

确实,因为我和巨人在一起太久了,我忘了我的国人是和我一样小的。这些水手唯一能做的是在我的盒子顶部挖一个洞、帮我爬出来。我累坏了,不能走远。

他们把我带到他们的船长那儿。

"欢迎到我们船上来,"他和善地说,"你很幸运我们发现了你。我的人发现水里有一

survive v. continue to live. 存在, 继续生存。**middle** n. the central part. 中央, 中间。**lose** v. fail to find. 丢失, 找不到。**fasten** v. fix sth firmly. 固定某物。**get out**(**of sth**)leave a place. 离开某处。

found you. My men saw that huge box on the water, and we decided to pull it along behind the ship. Then we realized there was a man inside! Why were you locked up in there? Was it a punishment for some terrible crime? But tell me all about it later. Now you need to sleep, and then eat.'

When I told him my story, a few hours later, he found it difficult to believe. But after a while he began to accept that what I told him must be true.

'But why do you shout so loudly?' he asked. 'We can hear you perfectly well if you speak normally.'

'You see,' I explained, 'for two years I've had to shout to make myself understood by the giants. I was like a man in the street who was trying to talk to another man at the top of a very tall building. And another thing — your sailors all seem very small to me, because I've been used to looking up at people twenty metres tall.'

He shook his head. 'Well, what a story! I think you should write a book about it when you get home.'

I stayed on the ship for several months, as we sailed slowly home to England. Finally, we arrived in Bristol on June 3rd, 1706. When I reached home, my wife made me promise never to go to sea again, and I thought my adventures had come to an end.

个大盒子,我们决定将它挂在轮船后面拖着走。然后我们意识到里面有一个人!你为什么被锁在里面?这是一种对什么可怕的罪过的惩罚吗?不过以后再告诉我这些,你现在需要休息,然后吃点东西。"

几个小时之后,我告诉他我的经历,他觉得难以置信。不过过了一会儿他开始接受我所告诉他的是真的。

"可是你为什么叫喊那么大声音?"他问,"如果你正常地说话我们也能听得很清楚。"

"你看,"我解释说,"两年来我不得不大声喊叫以便让我能被巨人听清楚。我就像一个走在大街上的人,要跟在一座非常高的建筑物顶上的另一个人说话。还有一件事,你的水手在我看起来都非常小,因为我以经习惯了仰着头看 20 米高的人。"

他摇着头。"嗯,多么好的故事啊!我觉得你回家后应该把它写成一本书。"

我们慢慢地航行回英国,我在这船上呆了几个月。最后我们于 1706 年 6 月 3 日到达布里斯托尔。我回到家时,我妻子要我许愿再也不出海,我想我的历险到此为止了。

man n. male person under the authority of sb else.(男性的)下属。**punishment** n. penalty inflicted on sb who has done sth wrong. 处罚,惩罚。**ask** v. request information. 问;询问。**be used to doing sth** having learned to accept sth. 习惯于,适应于。

10
The flying island of Laputa

I had only been at home for about ten days when a friend of mine asked me to join him on a journey to the East Indies. I still wanted to see more of the world, and as he was offering to give me double the usual pay, I managed to persuade my wife to let me go. The voyage took eight months, and after stopping for a short time in Malaysia, we arrived in the Gulf of Tongking.

'I'll have to stay here for a while on business,' my friend the captain told me. 'But you can take the ship and some of the sailors. Go and see what you can buy and sell in the islands around here.' That sounded interesting to me, so I agreed.

Unfortunately, we sailed straight into a terrible storm, which drove us many miles eastward. Then, by a very unlucky chance, we were seen and chased by two pirate ships. Our ship was not fast enough to escape, and the pirates caught us. They decided to keep the sailors to help sail the ship, but they did not need me. I suppose I was lucky they did not kill me. Instead, they left me alone in a small boat in the middle of the ocean, with only enough food for a few days, while they sailed away.

I am sure the pirates thought I would die. However, I saw land some hours later, and I managed to sail the boat to it. As I stepped out of the boat and walked up the beach, I noticed

10　　勒皮他飞岛

我在家里呆了只有 10 天,就有一个朋友请我加入他的到东印度群岛的旅行。我仍然想见更多的世面,而且他给我高出平常两倍的报酬,我说服了妻子让我去。航行了 8 个月,在马来西亚短暂停留之后,我们到达了东京湾。

"由于生意关系,我需要在这儿停一阵,"我的船长朋友对我说,"不过你可以用这只船和几个水手,去周围的岛屿转转,看你能买卖些什么。"这对我来说挺有意思,所以我就同意了。

不幸的是,我们径直驶进了一个可怕的风暴中,风暴将我们向东刮了许多英里。然后,由于极为不幸的巧合,我们被两只海盗船发现而被追逐。我们的船不够快,逃不了,海盗们抓住了我们。他们决定留下水手帮他们驾船,可是他们不需要我。我料想我真走运他们没有杀我。他们把我独自留在汪洋大海中的一只小船里,食物只够吃几天,他们自己则扬帆而去。

我敢肯定海盗们以为我必死无疑,但是,几个小时以后我看见了陆地,我让小船驶过去。当我跨出小船,走上海滩,我注意

fly *v*. move through the air. 飞。**double** *n*. something that is twice another in quantity. 双倍,两倍。**sound** *v*. seem when heard. 听起来。**straight** *ad*. directly. 直接地。**terrible** *a*. causing great fear. 可怕的,吓人的。

that although the sun had been very hot, the air suddenly seemed cooler. At first I thought a cloud was passing over the sun. But when I looked up, I saw, to my great astonishment, a large island in the sky, between me and the sun. It was moving towards me, and there were people running around on it. I waved my arms and shouted as loudly as possible. 'Help! Help! ' I cried. 'Rescue me! '

When the island was about a hundred metres over my head, they let down a seat on a chain. I sat on it, and was pulled up to the island. I had discovered the flying island of Laputa.

Laputans are certainly strange-looking people. Their heads always turn either to right or left: one of their eyes turns inwards, the other upwards. Their main interests are music and mathematics. They spend so much time thinking about mathematical problems that they do not notice what is happening around them. In fact, rich Laputans employ a servant whose job is to follow his master everywhere. The servant warns him if he is going to step into a hole, and reminds him to reply if someone speaks to him.

I was taken to see the King, but had to wait for at least an hour while he struggled with a difficult mathematical question. However, when he had finished, he spoke politely to me, and ordered his servants to show me to a room. For dinner they gave me three kinds of meat — a square of beef, a triangle of chicken and a circle of lamb. Even the bread was cut into mathematical shapes. In the evening a teacher arrived to help

到尽管太阳很热,空气却突然变凉了。起初我还以为是云遮了太阳,但是当我一抬头,令我极为惊讶的是,我看见天空中有一个大岛在我和太阳之间,它正向我移来,上面有人在四处跑动。我挥着手臂,尽可能大声地喊。"救命! 救命!"我叫道。"救救我!"

当岛屿在我头上大约 100 米高时,他们放下一个拴在链条上的坐椅。我坐在上面,被拉上了岛屿。我发现了勒皮他飞岛。

勒皮他人绝对是长相奇怪的人。他们的头总是或者向左或者向右转,他们的眼睛一只朝里一只朝外。他们的主要兴趣是音乐和数学,他们把大部分时间都花在思考数学问题上,以致于他们周围发生的事他们都没注意到。事实上,富有的勒皮他人请了个仆人,职责就是跟着主人到处走。仆人警示他是否要踩进坑里,如果有人跟他说话则提醒他回答。

我被带去见国王,可是我不得不等了至少一个小时,因为他在思考一个很难的数学问题。不过在他完成以后,他对我说话很礼貌,叫他的仆人带我去一个房间。晚餐他们给我 3 种肉 —— 一块方形牛肉、一块三角形鸡肉和一块圆形羊肉。甚至面包也是切成了数学形状。晚上一个教师来教我学

wave *v*. move one's hand as a signal. 向…挥手. **rescue** *v*. save sb from danger. 搭救, 救出. **seat** *n*. thing made or used for sitting on. 坐具. **music** *n*. art of arranging the sounds of voices or instrument. 音乐. **wait** *v*. stay somewhere without doing anything until sb comes. 等, 等候.

me learn the language, and in a few days I was able to make conversation with the island people.

Laputa is a circle of land, about eight kilometres across, covered with houses and other buildings. It is moved by a simple machine which uses magnets to pull the island closer to land or push it higher into the sky. The island always moves slowly. It can only fly over the country called Balnibarbi, which belongs to the King of Laputa.

It is difficult talking to Laputans, as they have little interest in anything except music and mathematics. They are, however, very worried about the future of the earth, the sun, and the stars, and they often discuss this. I heard a conversation about this shortly before I left Laputa.

'How are you, my friend?' one man asked another.

'As well as can be expected,' came the reply.

'And how is the sun, do you think?'

'I thought he looked rather feverish this morning. I'm afraid he'll get too hot and destroy himself one day, if he goes on like this.'

'I know, it's very worrying. And what about the earth? It's only thirty years until the next falling star comes this way, and the earth was very nearly destroyed by the last one!'

'That's right. We know that the next falling star is almost certain to get too close to the sun, and catch fire! And when the earth passes through that fire, it'll be destroyed immediately!'

他们的语言,几天后我就能够跟岛民交谈了。

勒皮他是一个圆形陆地,直径大约 8 公里,上面建有房屋和其他建筑。勒皮他岛用一个简单的机器移动,通过磁力把岛拉近地面或者是推向高空。这个岛总是慢慢地移动,它只能在一个叫巴尔尼巴比的国土上飞,那是属于勒皮他国王的。

跟勒皮他人谈话很困难,因为他们对除了音乐和数学之外的事没有兴趣。但是他们对地球、太阳和星星的未来很是担忧,经常讨论。在我快要离开勒皮他之前我听到了关于这事的谈话。

"你怎么样,我的朋友?"一个人对另一个问好。

"和预计的差不多。"他回答。

"太阳怎么样,你觉得?"

"我觉得今天早上他看起来有点发烧。如果继续下去,我担心他有朝一日会太烫而毁了自己。"

"我知道,他确实令人担心,地球怎么样?只有 30 年下一个流星就会掉过来,而上次差点把地球都毁灭了!"

"对,我们知道下一个掉下来的星星几乎肯定会与太阳靠得太近而着火。地球从火中穿过就会立即被摧毁!"

learn *v*. gain knowledge. 学,学习。**a few** not many. 不多。**be able to** have the knowledge to do sth. 有能力,能够…的。**machine** *n*. apparatus with several moving part. 机器,机械。**be worry about** be anxious. 焦虑,担忧。**feverish** *a*. having a fever. 发烧。

'Only thirty years! That's not much to look forward to, is it?' And the two men shook their heads sadly.

After several months on the island, I asked if I could visit the country underneath us. The King agreed, and ordered his officials to put me down on Balnibarbi, and show me round the capital, Lagado.

The most interesting place I saw there was the university, which was full of very clever men, with very clever ideas. They were all working hard to find better, faster, cheaper, easier ways of doing and making things. They had ideas for building houses from the roof downwards, turning rocks into soft material, making rivers run uphill, and saving sunshine in bottles. I cannot remember half of the astonishingly clever ideas which they were working on. One day, they told me, they would find the answers to all these problems, and then their country would be the most wonderful place in the world. Meanwhile, I noticed that the people looked hungry and miserable. Their clothes were old and full of holes, their houses were badly built and falling down. There were no vegetables or corn growing in the fields.

When I visited the School of Mathematics, I could not understand why the students looked so unhappy.

'What's the matter, young man?' I asked one of them. 'You look quite ill.'

'Yes, sir,' he answered. 'You see, we've only just eaten our lessons for today, and it's made us feel rather sick.'

"只有30年!不用等多长时间,对吧?"两个人忧伤地摇着头。

在岛上几个月后,我问我是否可以去拜访我们下面的国土。国王同意了,他命令他的官员把我放到下面的巴尔尼巴比,带我参观都城拉格多。

我在那儿看到的最有意思的地方是大学,那里极为聪明的人才济济一堂,想法也是极为聪明。他们都在努力工作以寻求更好、更快、更廉价、更简便的方法做事或制造东西。他们的主意有从屋顶向下建造房屋,把石头变成软物质、让河流上山坡、把阳光储蓄在瓶子里。他们正在酝酿着的令人惊诧不已的聪明想法我一半也记不住。有一天,他们告诉我,他们将会找到所有这些问题的答案,那时他们的国家将是世界上最美妙的地方。同时,我注意到人们饥饿而可怜,他们的衣服陈旧,满是破洞,他们的房子建造得很差,快要坍塌。田野里也没有蔬菜或谷物生长。

我访问数学院时,我不理解学生们为什么看起来那么不开心。

"怎么回事,年轻人?"我问其中一个,"你看起来病得利害。"

"是的,先生。"他回答说,"你看,我们只是吃了今天的课程,这令我们感到有点生病似的。"

downwards *a.* moving to what is lower. 向下。**remember** *v.* keep in memory. 记着。**look forward to** expect something that is going to happen. 盼望。期待。**order** *v.* command. 命令,指令。

'*Eaten* them?' I repeated in surprise. 'Why did you do that?'

'Oh, that's the way we learn here, sir,' he replied. 'Our professors write mathematical questions and answers on paper, then we eat the paper. After that we're only supposed to have bread and water for three days, while the information moves upwards to our heads. But it's awful, sir, not eating much for three days. And we often feel sick. Er... excuse me, sir!' And he ran past me out of the room. This highly developed system of teaching did not seem to be working well.

"吃课程?"我惊讶地重复,"你们为什么那样做?"

"噢,那是我们在这儿学习的方法,先生。"他回答,"我们的教授在纸上写上数学问题和解答,然后我们把纸吃下去。这以后在信息向上进入我们的脑子的过程中,我们只能有 3 天的面包和水。可是 3 天不吃多少东西真是可怕,先生,我们经常感到要病倒似的。嗯……对不起,先生!"他从我身边跑了出去。这个高度发达的教学体制似乎效果并不好。

paper *n*. substance made in thin sheets from wood pulp or rag and used for writing. 纸。**developed** *a*. advanced; mature. 先进的;成熟的。

101

11
Glubbdubdrib and Luggnagg

A lthough the Laputans were kind to me, I did not want to spend a long time in their country. Therefore, I decided to travel from Balnibarbi to the island of Luggnagg, from there to Japan, and then home to England. But before I went to Luggnagg, an official I had met in Lagado persuaded me to visit the small island of Glubbdubdrib.

'You'll find it a very interesting place,' he told me. 'Glubbdubdrib means the island of magicians. All the important people there are good at magic, you see. The President is the best magician of them all. But I must warn you, he has some very strange servants — they're all ghosts! By using magic he can order the ghost of any dead person to be his servant for twenty-four hours, and the ghost must obey.'

It seemed unbelievable, but it was true. When we arrived on the island, we were invited to the President's palace. His servants certainly looked strange to me — there was a smell of death about them. When the President no longer needed them, he waved a hand, and they simply disappeared.

I visited the President every day during my stay, and soon got used to seeing the ghosts. One day the President said, 'Gulliver, would you like to call a ghost? It could be anyone from the beginning of the world up to the present day. You could ask them questions about their lives. And you can be

11 格勒大锥和拉格奈格

尽管勒皮他人对我很和善，我并不想在这个国家呆多长时间，所以我决定从巴尔尼巴比旅行到拉格奈格岛，从那儿到日本，然后回到英国。可是在我去拉格奈格以前我在拉格多见到的一个官员说服我去参观格勒大锥小岛。

"你会发现那是一个非常有意思的地方。"他告诉我，"格勒大锥的意思是魔术师之岛，那儿所有的重要人物都擅长魔术，你明白吧。总统是他们中间最好的魔术师，但是我得警告你，他有一些非常奇怪的仆人——他们是鬼魂！他可以用魔法命令任何一个死去的人的鬼魂给他当24小时的仆人，而且鬼魂必须服从。"

这似乎难以置信，却是真的。我们到达岛上，被邀请到总统的宫里去。他的仆人在我看来绝对很古怪——他们有种死人的气味。当总统不再需要他们时，他一挥手他们就简单地不见了。

我在逗留期间天天去拜访总统，不久就习惯了看鬼魂。有一天总统说，"格列佛，你想不想叫一个鬼魂来？可以从世界开始那一时刻起直到现在的任何一个。你可以问他们关于他们一生的问题。而且你可以肯定

persuade *v*. cause sb to do sth by reasoning with him. 劝说某人做某事. **interesting** *a*. which take one's interest. 有趣的. **strange** *a*. unusual; surprising. 奇异的,奇怪的;奇特的. **obey** *v*. do what one is asked by sb.服从,顺从.

sure they'll tell the truth — ghosts always do.'

'That's very kind of you, sir,' I replied, and thought hard for a moment. 'First, I'd like to see Alexander the Great, please.'

The President pointed out of the window. There in a large field was the ghost of Alexander, with his huge army. This famous king lived long ago in Macedonia in northern Greece. His kingdom covered many countries, from Greece to Egypt, from Persia to parts of India. But he died very young, when he was only thirty-three, and no one knew why. The President called him into the room.

'Great King,' I said to him, 'just tell me one thing. Were you murdered, or did you die naturally?'

'Young man,' he replied, 'nobody murdered me. I drank too much and died of a fever.'

So, in these few words, I had learnt one of the secrets of history! I turned to the President. 'And now, may we see Julius Caesar and Brutus?'

The two Romans took Alexander's place. Brutus, of course, had killed Julius Caesar in Rome on 15th March, 44BC—one of the most famous murders in history. It is terrible to die by the hand of a friend.

'Great Caesar,' I said, 'how do you feel about your murderer, Brutus?'

'Do not call him that,' replied Caesar. 'He is a brave, good man, the best in Rome, and he did the right thing for

他们会告诉实情 —— 鬼魂总是这样的。"

"非常感谢你,先生。"我回答说,费力地考虑了一会,"首先,我想见亚历山大大帝,拜托。"

总统向窗外一指,那儿,在一个大的战场上出现了亚历山大大帝的鬼魂,以及他庞大的军队。这个伟大的国王很久以前生活在北希腊的马其顿。他的王国包括许多国家,从希腊到埃及,从波斯到印度的部分地区,但是他很年轻就死了,只活了33岁,谁也不知道为什么。总统叫他进屋来。

"伟大的国王,"我对他说,"只告诉我一件事,你是被谋杀的还是自然死亡?"

"年轻人,"他回答说,"没有人谋杀我,我喝得太多,死于热病。"

这样,就这几句话,我得知了历史上的一大秘密!我转向总统,"现在,我们可以见尤里乌斯·凯撒和布鲁图吗?"

这两个罗马人站到了亚历山大的地方。当然,布鲁图于公元前44年3月15日在罗马杀死了尤里乌斯·凯撒 —— 历史上最为有名的谋杀之一。死于朋友之手太可怕了。

"伟大的凯撒,"我说,"你对你的谋杀者布鲁图怎么看?"

"不要那样叫他,"凯撒回答,"他是一个勇敢的好人,罗马最优秀的人,他杀死我

tell *v*. make sth known in words to sb. 告诉,告知。
reply *v*. answer. 回答。
ago *ad*. in the past. 从前。
kingdom *n*. country ruled by a king. 王国。**young** *a*. not far advanced in life. 年轻的,幼小的。**brave** *a*. courageous. 勇敢的,无畏的。

105

Rome by killing me. In death, as in life, he has always been my friend. '

I cannot remember how many more ghosts I called to appear. I was very interested in their answers to my questions, which often seemed to offer a different view of history from the one I had been taught at school.

However, it was soon time to leave Glubbdubdrib, and sail to Luggnagg, a much larger island to the south-east of Japan. The Luggnuggians are polite and generous people, and I stayed here for three months. I made many friends among them. One day, one of them asked me, 'Have you ever seen any of our Struldbrugs?'

'I don't think so,' I replied. 'What's that?'

'Well, a Struldbrug is a human being who will never die, but will live for ever. If a Luggnuggian baby is born with a round spot above its left eye, which never disappears, it's a Struldbrug. We have over a thousand of them in the country. '

'How wonderful! ' I cried. 'How exciting! How lucky you are in Luggnagg, where a child has a chance of living for ever! And how especially lucky the Struldbrugs are! Disease, disaster, and death can never touch them! And imagine how much we can learn from them! I expect they're among the most important people in the country. They've lived through history and know so much, which they're certain to pass on to the rest of us. If I had the chance, I'd like to spend my whole life listening to the intelligent conversation of these extraordinary

为罗马做了一件正确的事。身后和生前一样，他永远是我的朋友。"

　　我不记得我还叫了多少鬼魂现身，我对他们对我问题的回答非常感兴趣，这些回答似乎提供了一种对历史的看法，经常与学校所教的毫不相同。

　　但是很快就到了该离开格勒大锥、驶向拉格奈格的时间，一个在日本东南、大得多的岛屿。拉格奈格人是有礼貌而慷慨大方的人民，我在那儿呆了3个月。我交了许多朋友。一天，有一个朋友问我，"你见过了我们的斯特鲁布鲁格没有？"

　　"我想没有。"我回答说，"那是什么？"

　　"噢，斯特鲁布鲁格是长生不死的人，如果一个拉格奈格婴儿生下来时左眼上有一个圆点，而且圆点是永不消失的，那么这个婴儿就是个斯特鲁布鲁格。我们国家有1 000多个这样的人。"

　　"多么美妙啊！"我叫道，"多么令人兴奋！你们在拉格奈格多么幸运，孩子有机会永生！这些斯特鲁布鲁格是多么特别的运气呀！疾病、灾难和死亡不能奈何他们！你想想我们可以从他们那儿学到多少东西！我想他们是这个国家最重要的人。他们活了这么多年，知道多少的东西，他们肯定要传播给其余的人。如果我有机会，我愿意整个一生都来听这些不同寻常的人的睿智的

be interested in concerned. 感兴趣。**view** *n*. a personal opinion. 见解，信念。**generous** *a*. given freely. 慷慨给予的。**baby** *n*. very young child. 婴儿。**disappear** *v*. go out of sight. 不见，消失。

people, here in Luggnagg!'

'Well, of course,' answered my Luggnuggian friend with a smile, 'we'll be delighted if you stay longer with us. But I'd like to know how *you* would plan your life if *you* were a Struldbrug.'

'That's easy,' I replied. 'First I'd work hard, and earn a lot of money. In about two hundred years I'd be the richest man in Luggnagg. I'd study too, so that I knew more about everything than the cleverest professors. I'd also write down everything important that happened over the years, so that students of history would come to me for help. I'd teach young people what I had learnt. But most of my time I'd spend with other Struldbrugs, friends of mine. Together we could help to destroy crime in the world, and begin to build a new and better life for everyone.'

I had only just finished describing the happiness of endless life, when I realized that my friend's shoulders were shaking and tears of laughter were running down his face.

'I really must explain,' he said. 'You see, you've made a very understandable mistake. You suppose that if someone lives for ever, he is young, healthy, and strong for ever too. And that doesn't happen. Our Struldbrugs have a terrible life. After living for about eighty years, they become ill and miserable. They have no friends and they can't remember much of the past. At that age the law considers them to be dead, so their children inherit their houses and money. Then they

谈话,就在拉格奈格!"

"噢,当然,"我的拉格奈格朋友笑着回答,"我们将很高兴如果你和我们呆久一点。不过我想知道如果你是个斯特鲁布鲁格的话,你将怎样安排你的生活。"

"那很容易。"我回答,"首先我将努力工作,挣许多钱。用近200年的时间我将成为拉格奈格最富有的人。我也将学习,这样我比最聪明的教授知道的都还多。我也会记下这些年里发生的每一件重大的事情,这样历史学者也会向我求助。我要教年轻人我所学到的。不过大多数时间我将与其他斯特鲁布鲁格,我的朋友,一起度过,我们一起可以帮助消灭世界上的犯罪,开始为每一个人建立新的更好的生活。"

我刚刚描绘完无尽生活的幸福,才发现我的朋友的肩膀抖动、笑得泪水都流到了脸上。

"我必须说明,"我朋友说,"你看,你犯了一个可以理解的错误。你以为如果一个人永远活着,他也永远年轻、健康而且强壮。可是那并没有发生。我们的斯特鲁布鲁格生活很可怕。在活了大约80年后,他们变得多病而悲惨。他们没有朋友,也记不住过去。在这个岁数法律认定他们已经死了,所以他们的孩子继承了他们的房屋和钱财。

important *a*. of great concern. 重要的,重大的。
shake *v*. move quickly and often jerkily from side to side. 急速摇动。**consider** *v*. think about. 考虑,思考。**inherit** *v*. receive as a result of the death of the previous owner. 继承。

sometimes have to beg to get enough food to eat. They lose their teeth and hair, they forget the names of their families, and the only thing they want is to die. But that's impossible!'

I realized how stupid I had been, and felt very sorry for the poor Struldbrugs.

I finally left Luggnagg on a boat sailing to Japan. From there I found a ship which was returning to England. My voyage to Laputa, Balnibarbi, Glubbdubdrib and Luggnagg had taken me away from home for five and a half years.

这样他们有时候不得不乞讨以搞到足够的东西吃。他们掉了牙齿和头发,他们忘记了他们家族的名字,他们唯一想要的就是死去。但是那不可能!"

我明白了我是多么愚蠢,为可怜的斯特鲁布鲁格感到难过。

最后我乘了一只驶往日本的船离开了拉格奈格。我在那儿找到了一艘正要回英国的船。我到勒皮他、巴尔尼巴比、格勒大锥和拉格奈格的航行使我离开家已经五年半了。

---

sorry *a*. feeling sad 感到遗憾,感到悲伤。**feel sorry for sb** feel sympathy for sb. 对…表示同情。

12

A voyage to the country of
the Houyhnhnme

It was not long before I started my next voyage, on 7th September, 1710, as captain of my own ship this time. The owner of the ship wanted me to sail to the Indian Ocean to do some business for him there, but I was very unlucky. On the way, I had to employ some new sailors from Barbados, but they were men of very bad character. I heard them whispering to the other sailors several times, but I did not suspect what they were planning. One morning, as we were sailing round the Cape of Good Hope, they attacked me and tied me up. They told me they were going to take control of the ship and become pirates. There was nothing I could do. They left me, alone, on the beach of a small island in the middle of the Indian Ocean.

As the ship sailed away, I realized I had no idea where I was. I found a road away from the beach, and walked very quietly and carefully along, in case I was attacked. Several strange-looking animals were lying in a field, and some were sitting in a tree. Their heads and chests were covered in hair, and they had beards as well. They walked sometimes on two, and sometimes on four legs, and could climb trees. They were certainly the ugliest animals I had ever seen in all my travels.

When I met one of these creatures on the road, his face

12 到慧骃国的航行

没过多久我又开始了我的下一次航行，时间 1710 年 9 月 7 日，这次是作为自己轮船的船长。轮船的所有者希望我航行到印度洋在那儿给他做点事，可是我非常不走运。路上，我不得不在巴尔巴道斯雇一些新水手，可是他们都是品行很差的人。我听见他们跟别的水手私语了好几次，但是我没有怀疑到他们在策划阴谋。一天早上，当我们正绕过好望角时，他们袭击了我，把我绑了起来。他们告诉我他们将控制轮船去当海盗。我毫无办法。他们把我孤独地留在印度洋中的一个小岛的沙滩上。

当轮船驶开了，我才想起我不知身在何处。我找到了一条离开沙滩的路，静静地小心地走着，以防受到袭击。几个怪模怪样的动物躺在一块地里，有些坐在树上。他们的头和胸长着毛发，也有胡须。他们有时用两肢着地行走，有时用四肢，他们绝对是我在所有旅行中见到的最丑陋的动物。

当我在路上见到一只这种动物时，他脸

start *v.* set off. 出发，动身。**captain** *n.* person in charge of a ship. 船长。**unlucky** *a.* not lucky. 不幸，运气不佳。**employ** *v.* give work to sb. 雇用某人。**leave** *v.* allow to remain. 留下，剩下。**idea** *n.* a picture in the mind. 概念。**along** *ad.* forward. 向前。**meet** *v.* come together. 遇见，碰见。

showed great surprise and he lifted a foot high in the air. I did not know if he was going to attack me or not, but I hit him hard with the side of my sword. He screamed so loudly that all the other animals ran to help him. There were about forty of them around me. I kept them away by waving my sword in the air, but their wild cries frightened me, and the horrible smell from their bodies made me feel sick.

Suddenly they all ran away. I noticed that a horse was coming along the road, so I supposed the animals were afraid of him. The horse stopped when he saw me, and seemed very surprised. He neighed several times in a very intelligent, gentle way, and I almost wondered if he was speaking in his own language. When another horse came along, the two horses walked up and down together, while neighing to each other. They seemed like two important people discussing a difficult problem. I watched this with astonishment, and decided that if the animals in this country seemed so sensible, the human beings must be the most intelligent in the world.

The two horses then came close to me, looking at my face and clothes with great interest. They talked to each other again, and then the first horse made clear signs for me to follow him.

He led me to a long, low building. Inside there were several large airy rooms, with no furniture. Other horses were sitting or lying comfortably on the floor, on clean blankets. But where was the master of the house? Were these horses his ser-

上露出吃惊的表情,把一只脚高高地举在空中。我不知道他是否要袭击我。但是我用我的剑侧重重地打了他一下。他高声尖叫,其他动物都跑过来帮他。在我周围大约有40个这样的动物。我在空中挥舞着剑,让他们离开我,不过他们狂乱的叫声令我害怕,他们身上的可怕气味令我恶心。

忽然他们全都跑开了。我看见了一匹马从路上走了过来,所以我估计这些动物害怕他。马看见我时停了下来,似乎很吃惊。他以非常智慧、温柔的方式嘶叫了几下,我几乎在想他是否在用自己的语言说话。另外一匹马来了,两匹马一起走上走下,互相嘶叫。他们像似两个重要的人物在讨论一个难题。我惊讶地看着这一切,觉得如果这个国家的动物看来都这么理智,其人类必定是世界上最智慧的。

然后两匹马走近我,非常感兴趣地看着我的脸和衣服。他们又互相谈话,然后第一匹马作出明显的手势让我跟他走。

他把我带到了一个长而低矮的建筑前,里面有几个大而通风的房间,没有家具。其他的马正舒适地站着或躺在地板上、毯子上。可是房子的主人在哪儿?这些马是他

frighten v. fill with fear. 使惧怕,使惊恐。**suppose** v. consider as probable. 猜想,认为可能。**intelligent** a. having or showing intelligence. 聪明的,有头脑。**air** n. the space above the ground. 空中。**airy** a. having plenty of fresh air moving about. 通风良好的。**master** n. employer. 主人,雇主。

vants? I began to wonder if I was going mad. Then I realized that the house did not belong to a human, but to the horse who had brought me here. In this country, horses, not people, were in control.

I started learning a little of their language. Their word Houyhnhnm means a horse, and the word itself sounds very like the noise a horse makes. I found it very difficult to say this word, and so I decided to shorten it and call them Houys. Their servants were the horrible-looking animals I had seen earlier. They did all the hard work, and lived in dirty little rooms in another building, where they were tied to the walls. To my horror, these ugly animals, called Yahoos, had human faces which looked very similar to mine. I did not want anyone to think I was a Yahoo, so I tried to make it clear that my habits were very different from theirs. At least I was allowed to sleep in a separate room from them.

At first I thought I would die of hunger, as I could not eat the Yahoos' dirty meat or the Houys' grass and corn. But I soon learnt how to bake little cakes made of corn, which I ate with warm milk. Sometimes I caught a bird, and cooked it, or picked leaves of plants to eat with my bread.

My Houy master was very interested in me, and as soon as I could speak the language, he asked me to explain where I had come from.

'Well, master,' I neighed, 'I've come from a country on the other side of the world. And you may not believe this, but

的仆从吗？我开始想我是否疯啦。然后我意识到这房子不是属于一个人的，而是属于把我带到这儿来的这匹马，这个国家是由马，而不是人控制着。

我开始学了一点他们的语言。他们的词"慧骃"（"Houyhnhnm"）意思是马，词本身听起来也非常像马叫的声音。我感到非常难发这个词，所以我决定把它缩短叫他们"Houy"。他们的仆从是我先前见到的面目可憎的动物。他们干所有的重活，住在另一个建筑的肮脏小房间里，那儿他们被栓在墙壁上。令我恐怖的是，这些丑陋的动物，叫作耶胡，长着人类的脸，看起来跟我的非常相像。我不想让谁认为我是耶胡，所以我竭力表明我的习惯跟他们的大不一样。至少我被允许睡在一个和他们隔开的房间里。

起先我以为我会饿死，因为我既不能吃耶胡的脏肉，也不能吃慧骃的草料和谷物。不过我很快就学会了怎样用谷物烤小糕点，我和着热牛奶一起吃。有时我逮住一只鸟烧来吃，或者摘些植物叶来和着我的面包吃。

我的慧骃主人对我很感兴趣，一旦我会说他们的话，他就请我解释我是从哪儿来的。

"好的，主人，"我嘶叫，"我是从在世界的另一边的国家来的。也许你不信，在我的

building *n*. constructing house. 建筑。**ugly** *a*. unpleasant to look. 难看的，丑的。**hunger** *n*. the wish for food. 饥饿。**eat** *v*. take food into mouth. 吃。**bake** *v*. cook by dry heat in an oven.（在炉中）烘烤；焙。**neigh** *n*. long high-pitched cry of a horse. 马的嘶叫声。

in my country all the important people look like Yahoos.'

'But how is that possible?' he asked gently. 'Your Houys surely wouldn't allow unintelligent creatures like Yahoos to control the country.'

'It may seem strange,' I agreed, 'but you see, *I* was surprised to find that in *this* country the Houys are the sensitive and intelligent creatures. And if I'm lucky enough to return home, I'll tell my friends all about it. But I'm afraid they may accuse me of lying.'

My master looked quite worried. 'What is lying?' he asked.

In their language there is no word which means telling lies, and my master had great difficulty in understanding me. I tried to explain.

'Oh,' he answered, still unsure. 'But why does anyone tell a lie? There's no reason for doing it. We use language in this country in order to understand each other, and to give and receive information. If you don't tell the truth, how *can* people understand each other?'

I began to see how different Houy life was from what I was used to.

'But tell me,' he continued, 'about your country.'

I was delighted to describe recent English history to him, especially some of our most successful wars.

'But why does one country attack another?' he asked.

'There are many reasons,' I replied. 'A king or his lords

国家所有的重要人物都看起来像耶胡。"

"可是那怎么可能呢?"他温柔地问我,"你们慧骃肯定不会允许愚蠢的耶胡来控制国家。"

"也许这看起来有点奇怪,"我表示赞同,"可是你看,我发现在这个国家里慧骃是理智而智慧生物也很吃惊。如果我运气好能回到家,我会把这些都告诉我的朋友,不过我担心他们会说我在撒谎。"

我的主人看得出来相当担心。"什么是撒谎?"他问。

在他们的语言中没有撒谎一词,我的主人要理解我很困难。我尝试着解释。

"噢,"他回答,仍然不能肯定,"可是为什么要撒谎呢? 没有理由那样做。在这个国家我们用语言来相互理解,发出和接收信息。如果你不说真相,人们怎么能相互理解呢?"

我开始明白慧骃的生活跟我过去习惯的是多么不一样。

"告诉我,"他接着说,"关于你们国家的情况。"

我很高兴地向他描绘最近的英国历史,特别是一些我们最为成功的战争。

"可是为什么一个国家要攻击另一个国家?"他问。

"有许多理由。"我回答,"一个国王或

accuse v. say that sb has done wrong. 指责某人有错,指控。understand v. grasp the meaning. 懂,理解。each other pron. each of two. 两者。different a. not the same kind. 不同的,差异的。describe v. give a picture in words. 描写,叙述。

119

may want more land. Or there may be a difference of opinion between two countries: for example, whether uniforms should be black, white, red or grey. Sometimes we fight because the enemy's too strong, sometimes because he isn't strong enough. Sometimes our neighbours want the things we have, or have the things we want, so we both fight until they take ours or give us theirs. We often attack our best friend, if we want some of his land. There's always a war somewhere. For this reason, being a soldier is one of the best jobs you can have.'

'A soldier,' repeated my master. 'I'm not quite sure what that is.'

'A soldier is a Yahoo who works for his King and country. His orders are to kill as many people as he can,' I answered.

'People who've never hurt him?' asked the Houy.

'That's right,' I said, pleased that he seemed to understand at last. 'Soldiers have killed thousands of people in recent history.'

He shook his head and looked sad. 'I think you must be— what was your word? Ah yes—*lying* to me. How could you and your countrymen kill so many other Yahoos? And why would you want to?'

I smiled as I replied proudly, 'Sir, you don't know much about European war. With our guns and bullets and gunpowder we can destroy a thousand ships, a hundred cities, and twenty thousand men. You see, —'

者他的王公想得到更多的土地，或者两个国家意见有分歧，比如说，制服该是黑色、白色、红色还是灰色。有时候我们打仗是因为敌人太强大，有时候是因为他不够强大。有时候我们的邻居想要我们有的东西，或者是有我们想要的东西，所以我们打仗，直到他们拿走我们的，或者把他们的给我们。我们经常攻击我们最好的朋友，如果我们想要他的一些领土。某个地方总会有战争。因此，当个战士是你能得到的最好工作之一。"

"战士？"我的主人重复道，"我不太清楚那是什么。"

"战士是为他的国王和国家工作的耶胡。给他的命令是尽量杀人。"我回答。

"杀害从来没有伤害他的人？"慧骃问。

"对。"我说，高兴地看到他似乎终于理解了，"在最近的历史上战士已经杀死了成千上万的人。"

他摇着头，看上去很哀伤。"我想你一定在 —— 你们的词怎么说的？噢，对 —— 向我撒谎。你和你的国人怎么能杀死那么多耶胡呢？而你们又为什么想那样呢？"

我笑着骄傲地回答，"先生，你不太了解欧洲的战争。用我们的枪、子弹和火药我们可以摧毁 1 000 只轮船，100 座城池，2 万人。你看 ——"

example *n*. fact. 例子，例证。**neighbour** *n*. person living next to another. 邻居。**friend** *n*. person one likes. 朋友，友人。**reason** *n*. the cause of an event. 原因，理由。**pleased** *a*. feeling satisfaction. 高兴的，满意的。**countryman** *n*. a person from one's own country. 同胞。

'Be quiet!' he ordered. 'I've heard enough. I know Yahoos are bad, but I didn't realize they could possibly do such terrible things.'

After these conversations I began to wonder whether the Houys were right. Why do we humans so often fight wars and tell lies? Peace and truth began to seem more important than making war or making money. I became more and more used to the Houys' ideas and way of life. As the Houys did, I hated the Yahoos for their dirty habits and unpleasant character. By the time I had been there a year, I walked and neighed like the Houys. I felt such a strong love for them that I planned to spend the rest of my life among them, and to try to become more like them. It is a great sadness to me, even today, that this was not possible.

One day my Houy master said, 'Can you explain something to me? Why are the Yahoos so violently fond of those shining stones in the fields? They dig for days to get them out of the ground, and hide them jealously from other Yahoos.'

'I expect they've found pieces of gold or silver,' I said. Because he did not seem to understand, I added, 'We use them as money, to pay for things, you see.'

'How strange!' he replied. 'We share everything here. No Houy needs—what do you call it? —*money*.'

Perhaps you can imagine how I felt. I knew I could be happy for ever with these sensible, gentle creatures, who never lied or stole, in a country which had no disease, no crime, no

"安静点!"他命令道,"我听够了。我知道耶胡坏,可是我也没想到他们竟然会作出如此可怕的事。"

经过这些谈话后,我开始想慧骃是否是对的。为什么我们人类如此经常地进行战争和撒谎?和平和真话开始看起来比进行战争或挣钱更重要。我越来越习惯于慧骃的想法和生活方式。和慧骃一样,我也厌恶耶胡的脏习惯和令人不快的性格。到这时我已经在那儿一年了,我像慧骃那样走路和嘶叫。我对他们充满强烈的喜爱,我计划我的余生都和他们一起度过,并且变得更像他们。这没成为可能;即使今天也是我的一大憾事。

一天我的慧骃主人说,"你可以给我解释一些事吗?为什么耶胡如此狂热地喜欢田野里的那些闪亮的石头?他们连续多少天把它们从地里挖出来,小心翼翼地把它们藏起来不让别的耶胡发现。"

"我估计他们找到了金子或银子。"我说,因为他似乎还不理解,我又加了一句,"我们用来当钱花,来买东西,明白吧。"

"多奇怪!"他回答,"我们这儿什么都共享,没有慧骃需要 —— 你们叫它什么?—— 钱。"

也许你可以想象我的感受,我清楚,和这些理智、温顺的动物在一起,他们从不撒谎或偷盗,在一个没有疾病、没有犯罪、没有

quiet *a*. not making oneself noticed by activity. 安静的,不显眼的。 **money** *n*. wealth. 财富。 **make money** earn money. 挣钱,赚钱。 **character** *n*. qualities that make a person different from others. 特征,天性。 **explain** *v*. make sth clear. 解释,讲解。

wars. But this perfect happiness did not last long.

'I'm sorry,' said my master one day. 'My friends and I have decided you can't stay here any longer. You see, you're neither one of us, nor a Yahoo.'

'No!' I cried desperately. 'Don't send me away! How can I go back to England to live with those awful Yahoos!'

'I'm afraid you must,' he replied gently. 'My servants will help you make a boat.'

And so, two months later, although I was very sad to leave, I said goodbye to my dear master and his family, and rowed away from the land of the Houys. I knew that I would never find happiness anywhere else.

After several days travelling eastwards, I arrived in Australia, and from there managed to find a ship returning to Europe. I did not enjoy the voyage. The sailors all laughed at me because I walked and neighed like a horse. They looked just like those horrible Yahoos, and at first I could not let them touch me or come near me. Their ugly faces and unpleasant smell made me feel quite ill.

And when I arrived home in England, after being away for five years, my wife and children were delighted to see me, because they had thought I was dead. But to my horror they looked and smelt like Yahoos too, and I told them to keep away from me.

Even now, five years later, I do not let my children get close to me, although I sometimes allow my wife to sit with

战争的国家里,我将永远幸福。可是这种完美的幸福没有持续多长时间。

"我很抱歉,"一天我的主人说,"我的朋友和我已经决定,你不能在这儿呆下去了。你看,你既不是我们中的一员,也不是一个耶胡。"

"不!"我绝望地叫,"不要赶走我! 我怎么能回到英国去与那些可怕的耶胡住在一起呢!"

"我恐怕你必须走。"他温文尔雅地回答,"我的仆从会帮你造一只船。"

这样,两个月后,尽管我为离去感到悲伤,我还是告别了我的主人和他的一家,划船离开了慧骃国。我清楚我在别的地方再也不会找到幸福。

向东航行了几天后,我到达了澳大利亚,在那儿我找到了一艘返回欧洲的轮船。我不喜欢这旅行。水手们都嘲笑我,因为我像一匹马那样走路和嘶叫。他们就像那些可怕的耶胡,起初我不让他们碰我或者靠近我。他们丑陋的脸和令人不快的气味让我感到恶心。

当我到达在英格兰的家,在离开了 5 年后,我的妻子和儿女见到我非常高兴,因为他们以为我已经死了。令我感到恐惧的是,他们看起来、嗅起来也像耶胡,我叫他们离我远点。

即使现在,5 年以后,我还是不让我的孩子靠近我,尽管我有时让我的妻子在我吃饭

happiness *n*. fortune. 幸运。**cry** *v*. call out loudly in words. 高声喊叫,呼喊。**find** *v*. discover. 意外,发现,撞见。**last long** continuing for a long time. 持久。**neither...nor** not one and not the other of two. 既非此又非彼。

125

me while I eat. I try to accept my countrymen now, but the proud ones, who are so full of their own self-importance — well, they had better not come near me. How sad that people cannot learn from the Houys! I was hoping that perhaps human beings would change their ways after reading the stories of my life with the Houys. But they accuse me of lying in my book. And now I realize that people still lie, steal, and fight, just as they have always done, and probably will always do.

I will say no more. Clearly, there is no hope for human beings. I was stupid to think that I could bring reason and truth into their lives and thoughts. Humans are all Yahoos, and Yahoos they will remain.

时与我在一起坐一会儿。现在我力图接受我的国人,那些骄傲的除外,他们充满了自大的情绪 —— 他们最好不要走近我。人们不能向慧骃学习是多么令人忧伤! 我希望人类在读了我与慧骃在一起生活的故事后也许会改变他们的方式。可是他们指责我在书中撒谎。现在我意识到人们仍然在撒谎、抢劫和战争,正如他们一直所做的,而且也许永远会这样。

我不想再说什么。显然,人类是没有希望的。我真愚蠢,我以为我可以把理智和真相带到他们的生活和思想中去。人类都是耶胡,而且将永远是耶胡。

try *v*. make an attempt. 试做。**learn from** *v*. gain knowledge by study. 学习。**hope** *v*. desire for sth to happen. 希望。**lie** *v*. make a statement one knows to be untrue. 说谎,撒谎。

Exercises

A Checking your understanding

Chapters 1 - 4 *Are these sentences true (T) or false (F)?*

1 The King's officials found nothing in Gulliver's pockets.

2 Lilliputians called Gulliver the Man-Mountain.

3 Gulliver put on his glasses in order to see the Blefuscans better.

4 The King of Lilliput was angry because Gulliver refused to steal all the enemy's ships.

5 Flimnap and Reldresal were Gulliver's best friends

Chapters 5 - 9 *Write answers to these questions.*

1 How did Gulliver kill the rat in the bedroom?

2 Who saved Gulliver's life many times in Brobdingnag?

3 Why was the farmer pleased to sell Gulliver to the Queen?

4 What dangers were there for Gulliver at the palace? Find as many as you can.

5 Why did the King of Brobdingnag refuse to learn how to make gunpowder?

Chapters 10 - 12 *How much can you remember? Check your answers.*

1 What were the Laputans' two main interests?

2 How did Balnibarbi students learn their mathematics lessons?

3 What was strange about the President of Glubbdubdrib's

128

servants?

4 What was a Struldbrug?

5 What were the Houys' servants called, and who did they look like?

6 What were the three things that Gulliver's Houy master didn't understand?

B Working with language

1 *Put together these beginnings and endings of sentences. Check your answers in Chapter 1.*

1 Even my hair, which was long and thick,

2 The wind drove our ship on to a rock,

3 I was so exhausted that

4 As I stood up,

5 which broke the ship in half.

6 I lay down and went to sleep.

7 was tied to the ground.

8 I heard cries of astonishment all around me.

2 *Choose the best linking word and complete these sentences with information from the story.*

1 Gulliver escaped to Blefuscu from Lilliput because/although . . .

2 The dwarf was sent away from the palace before/after . . .

3 Gulliver spoke to several ghosts while/during . . .

4 Gulliver loved the Houys, so/then . . .

C Activities

1 Which of Gulliver's voyages did you enjoy most? Or, which of these countries would you most like to visit? Say which one, and explain why.

2 You are a television news reporter. Interview Gulliver after his return from the country of the Houys. Write down your conversation, and act it out with a partner if possible.

3 What do you think Gulliver would find strange or interesting about your country today? Imagine that he is visiting your country for the first time, and write about it from his point of view. You could begin:

I found myself walking along a road. Suddenly I saw ...